時運壬寅

Moments of Luck

2022

Feng Shui and Ba Zi Calendar
for the
Year of the Water Tiger

Anne Rosa Wangnick

Impressum

Chinese Symbols used in the Title

時 Time 運 Luck 壬 Water 寅 Tiger (Chinese year 2022)

Disclaimer

The times of the moon phases, the year and month beginnings are calculated astronomically and are given in UTC. The author made significant efforts to produce a high quality, informative and helpful book. She nevertheless makes no statement nor gives warranties of any kind with regard to the completeness and accuracy of the contents of the book, nor for its suitability for any particular purpose. The usage of this book and the included information contained are under the sole responsibility of the reader. Neither the author nor the publisher accepts liability for any kind of losses or damages caused or alleged to be caused directly or indirectly from using the information contained herein. The author and publisher specifically disclaim all responsibility for any liability, loss, or risk, personal or otherwise, which may incur as a consequence, directly or indirectly, of the use and application of any of the contents of this book.

Copyright

Design, Layout, Photography, Cover Design

Anne Rosa Wangnick

ISBN 9798715115010

July 2021

Anne Rosa Wangnick Consulting
Lammersdorfer Str. 61
D-52159 Roetgen-Rott
tel: +49 (0)2471 134989
mail: anne@wangnick.com
www.wangnick.com

Introduction

The calendar 時運 **Moments of Luck** is based on the Chinese tong shu calendars. For every day you will find intuitive symbols for favorable and inauspicious actions according to popular eastern and western divination systems.

The Chinese view of the universe is based on the cosmic trinity

天	*tian*	*Heaven*	*use the suitable time*
人	*ren*	*Man*	*to do the right thing*
地	*di*	*Earth*	*at an appropriate place*

Man is the center of all contemplations, his luck and his personal well being. To get the best from heaven and earth it is necessary to do the right thing at the right place, since heaven and earth are combined by human deeds.

Even though this calendar looks unusual at the first glance, it is simple to use with increasing levels of complexity. Get accustomed to the different systems by using them successively.

The most important system is the *Moments of Luck* of day and hour together with the general quality of a day. It provides a step-by-step guide to select a fortunate date together with a suitable hour.

The *I Ching symbol* of the day outlines the theme of the day and is useful for meditation. Hint: Refer to books. So you get in touch with the most important wisdom of Chinese culture.

The tone *Nayin* describes the hidden energy of the day. How this tone effects you depends on your own tone. This system practices the five elements, the basis of all Chinese sciences.

Officers, lunar mansions, moon phases and *zodiac signs* are used to determine appropriate days for special events like marriage, project kick-off or burials.

To familiarize with *Feng Shui* and *Ba Zi*, read the notes about Feng Shui and Ba Zi of the year. The *Flying Stars* explain the energies of the compass directions. Consult them if you plan to travel or start constructions in home and garden. *Ming Gua* are your personal good and challenging directions and invite you to experiment. The *heavenly stem and earthly branch* of a Chinese day describes the day in terms of Yin/Yang and the five elements. Using your pillars of destiny you can estimate the day's effect on you.

In this booklet you do not only have plenty of space to add events, notes and ideas, but in addition a lot of explanations. I encourage you to consider the Chinese view of the universe from time to time. It will enrich your life.

Anne Rosa Wangnick

Rott (Eifel), April 2021

Calendar Structure

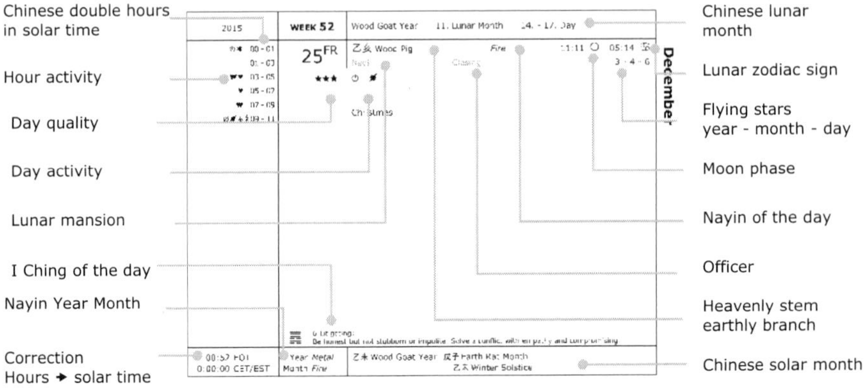

Auspicious	Activities	Avoid
✹	support	✹̸
❤❤	love, partnership, marriage	❤❤̸
♥	communication, negotiations, friends	♥̸
✈	travel	✈̸
⏻	start projects, business opening	⏻̸
€	money related affairs	€̸

Day Quality

ϟ	explosive energy
☆̸☆̸	very difficult day
☆̸	difficult day
★	average day
★★	good day
★★★	excellent day

Moon Phases

●	New Moon
☽	Waxing Moon
○	Full Moon
☾	Waning Moon

Zodiac Signs

♑	Capricorn	♋	Cancer
♒	Aquarius	♌	Leo
♓	Pisces	♍	Virgo
♈	Aries	♎	Libra
♉	Taurus	♏	Scorpio
♊	Gemini	♐	Sagittarius

Solar Time

Longitude correction .... min

www.wangnick.com/software_timecalculator.htm

Contents

Moments of Luck 2022

January 2022

1 Sa ⏻ New Year's Day

2 Su ●

3 Mo

4 Tu ⏻

5 We

6 Th Three Kings' Day

7 Fr € ⏻

8 Sa ♥ € ⏻ ✈

9 Su ♥ € ☽

10 Mo ♥ ✈

11 Tu ⏻

12 We ⏻ ✈

13 Th

14 Fr € ✈

15 Sa

16 Su ♥

17 Mo ⏻ ○

18 Tu

19 We €

20 Th ♥ € ⏻ ✈

21 Fr ♥ €

22 Sa ♥ ✈

23 Su ♥ ⏻

24 Mo ⏻ ✈

25 Tu ☾

26 We € ✈

27 Th

28 Fr ♥ ⏻

29 Sa

30 Su

31 Mo €

February 2022

1 Tu ♥ € ⏻ ✈ Chinese New Year ●

2 We ♥ €

3 Th ♥ ✈

4 Fr € ✈

5 Sa

6 Su ⏻ ✈

7 Mo

8 Tu € ✈ ☽

9 We

10 Th ♥

11 Fr

12 Sa ✈

13 Su ⏻

14 Mo ♥ ⏻ ✈ Valentine's Day

15 Tu ⏻

16 We € ✈ ○

17 Th

18 Fr ⏻ ✈

19 Sa

20 Su € ✈

21 Mo

22 Tu ♥ ⏻

23 We ⏻ ☾

24 Th ✈

25 Fr

26 Sa ♥ € ⏻ ✈

27 Su ⏻

28 Mo € ✈ Rose Monday

Moments of Luck 2022

March 2022

Day	Symbols	Holiday	Moon
1 Tu			
2 We	⏻ ✈	Ash Wednesday	●
3 Th			
4 Fr	€ ⏻ ✈		
5 Sa			
6 Su			
7 Mo	♥♥		
8 Tu	⏻		
9 We			
10 Th			☽
11 Fr	⏻		
12 Sa	€		
13 Su	♥♥ ✈		
14 Mo	⏻		
15 Tu	♥♥ ⏻ ✈		
16 We			
17 Th	€ ✈		
18 Fr			○
19 Sa	♥♥		
20 Su	⏻		
21 Mo			
22 Tu			
23 We	⏻		
24 Th	€		
25 Fr	♥♥ ✈		☾
26 Sa	♥♥ ⏻		
27 Su	⏻ ✈		
28 Mo			
29 Tu	€ ✈		
30 We			
31 Th	♥♥		

April 2022

Day	Symbols	Holiday	Moon
1 Fr	⏻		●
2 Sa			
3 Su			
4 Mo	⏻		
5 Tu	€ ⏻ ✈		
6 We	€		
7 Th	♥♥ € ⏻ ✈		
8 Fr	⏻		
9 Sa	✈		☽
10 Su			
11 Mo	€ ✈		
12 Tu	♥♥		
13 We	♥♥ ✈		
14 Th			
15 Fr		Good Friday	
16 Sa			○
17 Su	€ ⏻ ✈	Easter Sunday	
18 Mo	€	Easter Monday	
19 Tu	♥♥ € ⏻ ✈		
20 We	⏻		
21 Th	✈		
22 Fr			
23 Sa	€ ✈		☾
24 Su	♥♥		
25 Mo	♥♥ ✈		
26 Tu			
27 We	⏻		
28 Th			
29 Fr	€ ⏻ ✈		
30 Sa	€		●

Moments of Luck 2022

May 2022

Day	Symbols	Note	Moon
1 Su	♥ € ✈	Labour Day	
2 Mo	⏻		
3 Tu	✈		
4 We			
5 Th	€ ✈		
6 Fr	€ ⏻ ✈		
7 Sa	✈		
8 Su	♥ ⏻		
9 Mo			☽
10 Tu			
11 We			
12 Th	♥ € ✈		
13 Fr			
14 Sa	€ ✈		
15 Su			
16 Mo	⏻ ✈		○
17 Tu			
18 We	€ ⏻ ✈		
19 Th	✈		
20 Fr	♥		
21 Sa			
22 Su			☾
23 Mo			
24 Tu	♥ € ✈		
25 We			
26 Th	€ ⏻ ✈	Ascension	
27 Fr	♥		
28 Sa	⏻ ✈		
29 Su			
30 Mo	€ ✈		●
31 Tu	✈		

June 2022

Day	Symbols	Note	Moon
1 We	♥		
2 Th			
3 Fr			
4 Sa			
5 Su	♥ € ✈	Whit Sunday	
6 Mo	♥ € ⏻ ✈	Whit Monday	
7 Tu	€ ⏻		☽
8 We	♥ ✈		
9 Th	€ ⏻		
10 Fr	✈		
11 Sa			
12 Su	⏻ ✈		
13 Mo	♥		
14 Tu	♥ ⏻		○
15 We	⏻		
16 Th			
17 Fr			
18 Sa	♥ € ⏻ ✈		
19 Su	€ ⏻		
20 Mo	♥ ✈		
21 Tu	€ ⏻		☾
22 We	✈		
23 Th			
24 Fr	€ ⏻ ✈		
25 Sa	♥		
26 Su	♥		
27 Mo	⏻		
28 Tu			
29 We			●
30 Th	♥ € ⏻ ✈		

Moments of Luck 2022

July 2022

1 Fr	€ ⏻	
2 Sa	♥♥ ⏻ ✈	
3 Su	€ ⏻	
4 Mo	✈	
5 Tu		
6 We	€ ✈	
7 Th	€ ⏻ ✈	☽
8 Fr		
9 Sa		
10 Su	⏻	
11 Mo		
12 Tu	€	
13 We	♥♥ € ⏻ ✈	○
14 Th	♥♥ € ⏻	
15 Fr	✈	
16 Sa	€ ⏻	
17 Su	⏻ ✈	
18 Mo		
19 Tu	€ ✈	
20 We		☾
21 Th		
22 Fr		
23 Sa	♥♥	
24 Su	€	
25 Mo	♥♥ € ⏻ ✈	
26 Tu	♥♥ € ⏻	
27 We	⏻ ✈	
28 Th	♥♥ € ⏻	●
29 Fr	⏻ ✈	
30 Sa		
31 Su	€ ✈	

August 2022

1 Mo		
2 Tu		
3 We		
4 Th		
5 Fr	€	☽
6 Sa	♥♥ € ⏻ ✈	
7 Su	♥♥ € ⏻	
8 Mo		
9 Tu	✈	
10 We	€	
11 Th	⏻ ✈	
12 Fr		○
13 Sa	✈	
14 Su		
15 Mo		
16 Tu	€	
17 We	✈	
18 Th	⏻	
19 Fr	♥♥ € ⏻ ✈	☾
20 Sa		
21 Su	✈	
22 Mo	♥♥ €	
23 Tu	⏻ ✈	
24 We		
25 Th	€ ✈	
26 Fr		
27 Sa	⏻	●
28 Su	€	
29 Mo	✈	
30 Tu		
31 We	♥♥ € ⏻ ✈	

Moments of Luck 2022

September 2022

Day	Symbols	Moon
1 Th		
2 Fr	✈	
3 Sa	€	☽
4 Su	⏻ ✈	
5 Mo		
6 Tu	€ ⏻ ✈	
7 We		
8 Th		
9 Fr	♥♥ €	
10 Sa	⏻	○
11 Su		
12 Mo	€	
13 Tu	€ ⏻ ✈	
14 We	♥♥ € ⏻	
15 Th	♥♥ € ✈	
16 Fr	⏻ ✈	
17 Sa	✈	☾
18 Su	€	
19 Mo		
20 Tu		
21 We	♥♥ €	
22 Th	⏻	
23 Fr		
24 Sa	€	
25 Su	€ ⏻ ✈	●
26 Mo	♥♥ € ⏻	
27 Tu	♥♥ € ⏻ ✈	
28 We	♥♥ ⏻ ✈	
29 Th	✈	
30 Fr	€	

October 2022

Day	Symbols	Moon
1 Sa		
2 Su		
3 Mo	♥♥ €	☽
4 Tu	⏻	
5 We		
6 Th	€	
7 Fr	€ ⏻ ✈	
8 Sa	♥♥ € ⏻ ✈	
9 Su	€	○
10 Mo	♥♥ ⏻ ✈	
11 Tu	⏻	
12 We	⏻ ✈	
13 Th		
14 Fr	€ ⏻ ✈	
15 Sa	♥♥ €	
16 Su	♥♥	
17 Mo		☾
18 Tu	€	
19 We		
20 Th	♥♥ € ⏻ ✈	
21 Fr	€	
22 Sa	♥♥ € ✈	
23 Su	⏻	
24 Mo	⏻ ✈	
25 Tu		●
26 We	€ ✈	
27 Th	♥♥ €	
28 Fr	♥♥	
29 Sa		
30 Su	€ ⏻	
31 Mo Halloween		

Moments of Luck 2022

November 2022

Day	Symbols	Note	Moon
1 Tu	♥ € ⏻ ✈		☽
2 We	€		
3 Th	♥ € ⏻ ✈		
4 Fr	⏻		
5 Sa	⏻ ✈		
6 Su			
7 Mo			
8 Tu	€ ✈		○
9 We			
10 Th	♥		
11 Fr			
12 Sa	✈		
13 Su			
14 Mo	♥ € ⏻ ✈		
15 Tu	⏻		
16 We	€ ✈		☾
17 Th			
18 Fr			
19 Sa			
20 Su	♥ € ✈		
21 Mo			
22 Tu	♥		
23 We			●
24 Th	✈		
25 Fr			
26 Sa	♥ € ⏻ ✈		
27 Su	⏻	1. Advent	
28 Mo	€ ⏻ ✈		
29 Tu	♥		
30 We			☽

December 2022

Day	Symbols	Note	Moon
1 Th			
2 Fr	€ ✈		
3 Sa			
4 Su	♥	2. Advent	
5 Mo			
6 Tu	✈	Saint Nicholas	
7 We	⏻		
8 Th			○
9 Fr	♥ ⏻ ✈		
10 Sa	€ ⏻		
11 Su	♥ ✈	3. Advent	
12 Mo	⏻		
13 Tu	⏻ ✈		
14 We			
15 Th	€ ⏻ ✈		
16 Fr	♥		☾
17 Sa	♥ ⏻		
18 Su	⏻	4. Advent	
19 Mo			
20 Tu			
21 We	♥ € ⏻ ✈		
22 Th	€ ⏻		
23 Fr	♥ ✈		●
24 Sa	⏻	Christmas Eve	
25 Su	⏻ ✈	Christmas	
26 Mo			
27 Tu	€ ⏻ ✈		
28 We	♥		
29 Th	♥		
30 Fr	⏻		☽
31 Sa		New Year's Eve	

Moments of Luck 2023

January 2023

Day	Symbols	Holiday	Moon
1 Su		New Year's Day	
2 Mo	♥♥ € ⏻ ✈		
3 Tu	€ ⏻		
4 We	♥♥ ⏻ ✈		
5 Th	⏻		
6 Fr	€ ⏻	Three Kings' Day	○
7 Sa	✈		
8 Su			
9 Mo	€ ✈		
10 Tu			
11 We			
12 Th	⏻		
13 Fr			
14 Sa	€		
15 Su	♥♥ € ⏻ ✈		☾
16 Mo	♥♥ €		
17 Tu			
18 We	€ ⏻		
19 Th	♥♥ ✈		
20 Fr			
21 Sa	€ ✈		●
22 Su		Chinese New Year	
23 Mo	⏻		
24 Tu			
25 We			
26 Th	€		
27 Fr	♥♥ € ⏻ ✈		
28 Sa	♥♥ €		☽
29 Su			
30 Mo	€ ⏻		
31 Tu	✈		

February 2023

Day	Symbols	Holiday	Moon
1 We			
2 Th	€ ⏻ ✈		
3 Fr			
4 Sa	✈		
5 Su			○
6 Mo			
7 Tu			
8 We	⏻		
9 Th	♥♥ ✈		
10 Fr	⏻		
11 Sa	€ ✈		
12 Su			
13 Mo	⏻ ✈		☾
14 Tu		Valentine's Day	
15 We	€ ✈		
16 Th	✈		
17 Fr	⏻		
18 Sa	⏻		
19 Su	♥♥		
20 Mo		Rose Monday	●
21 Tu	♥♥ € ✈		
22 We	⏻	Ash Wednesday	
23 Th	€ ✈		
24 Fr			
25 Sa	⏻ ✈		
26 Su			
27 Mo	€ ⏻ ✈		☽
28 Tu	✈		

Overview

2022

January

Wk	52	1	2	3	4	5
Mo		3	10	17	24	31
Tu		4	11	18	25	
We		5	12	19	26	
Th		6	13	20	27	
Fr		7	14	21	28	
Sa	1	8	15	22	29	
Su	2	9	16	23	30	

February

Wk	5	6	7	8	9
Mo		7	14	21	28
Tu	1	8	15	22	
We	2	9	16	23	
Th	3	10	17	24	
Fr	4	11	18	25	
Sa	5	12	19	26	
Su	6	13	20	27	

March

Wk	9	10	11	12	13
Mo		7	14	21	28
Tu	1	8	15	22	29
We	2	9	16	23	30
Th	3	10	17	24	31
Fr	4	11	18	25	
Sa	5	12	19	26	
Su	6	13	20	27	

April

Wk	13	14	15	16	17
Mo		4	11	18	25
Tu		5	12	19	26
We		6	13	20	27
Th		7	14	21	28
Fr	1	8	15	22	29
Sa	2	9	16	23	30
Su	3	10	17	24	

May

Wk	17	18	19	20	21	22
Mo		2	9	16	23	30
Tu		3	10	17	24	31
We		4	11	18	25	
Th		5	12	19	26	
Fr		6	13	20	27	
Sa		7	14	21	28	
Su	1	8	15	22	29	

June

Wk	22	23	24	25	26
Mo		6	13	20	27
Tu		7	14	21	28
We	1	8	15	22	29
Th	2	9	16	23	30
Fr	3	10	17	24	
Sa	4	11	18	25	
Su	5	12	19	26	

July

Wk	26	27	28	29	30
Mo		4	11	18	25
Tu		5	12	19	26
We		6	13	20	27
Th		7	14	21	28
Fr	1	8	15	22	29
Sa	2	9	16	23	30
Su	3	10	17	24	31

August

Wk	31	32	33	34	35
Mo	1	8	15	22	29
Tu	2	9	16	23	30
We	3	10	17	24	31
Th	4	11	18	25	
Fr	5	12	19	26	
Sa	6	13	20	27	
Su	7	14	21	28	

September

Wk	35	36	37	38	39
Mo		5	12	19	26
Tu		6	13	20	27
We		7	14	21	28
Th	1	8	15	22	29
Fr	2	9	16	23	30
Sa	3	10	17	24	
Su	4	11	18	25	

October

Wk	39	40	41	42	43	44
Mo		3	10	17	24	31
Tu		4	11	18	25	
We		5	12	19	26	
Th		6	13	20	27	
Fr		7	14	21	28	
Sa	1	8	15	22	29	
Su	2	9	16	23	30	

November

Wk	44	45	46	47	48
Mo		7	14	21	28
Tu	1	8	15	22	29
We	2	9	16	23	30
Th	3	10	17	24	
Fr	4	11	18	25	
Sa	5	12	19	26	
Su	6	13	20	27	

December

Wk	48	49	50	51	52
Mo		5	12	19	26
Tu		6	13	20	27
We		7	14	21	28
Th	1	8	15	22	29
Fr	2	9	16	23	30
Sa	3	10	17	24	31
Su	4	11	18	25	

2023

January

Wk	52	1	2	3	4	5
Mo		2	9	16	23	30
Tu		3	10	17	24	31
We		4	11	18	25	
Th		5	12	19	26	
Fr		6	13	20	27	
Sa		7	14	21	28	
Su	1	8	15	22	29	

February

Wk	5	6	7	8	9
Mo		6	13	20	27
Tu		7	14	21	28
We	1	8	15	22	
Th	2	9	16	23	
Fr	3	10	17	24	
Sa	4	11	18	25	
Su	5	12	19	26	

March

Wk	9	10	11	12	13
Mo		6	13	20	27
Tu		7	14	21	28
We	1	8	15	22	29
Th	2	9	16	23	30
Fr	3	10	17	24	31
Sa	4	11	18	25	
Su	5	12	19	26	

April

Wk	13	14	15	16	17
Mo		3	10	17	24
Tu		4	11	18	25
We		5	12	19	26
Th		6	13	20	27
Fr		7	14	21	28
Sa	1	8	15	22	29
Su	2	9	16	23	30

May

Wk	18	19	20	21	22
Mo	1	8	15	22	29
Tu	2	9	16	23	30
We	3	10	17	24	31
Th	4	11	18	25	
Fr	5	12	19	26	
Sa	6	13	20	27	
Su	7	14	21	28	

June

Wk	22	23	24	25	26
Mo		5	12	19	26
Tu		6	13	20	27
We		7	14	21	28
Th	1	8	15	22	29
Fr	2	9	16	23	30
Sa	3	10	17	24	
Su	4	11	18	25	

July

Wk	26	27	28	29	30	31
Mo		3	10	17	24	31
Tu		4	11	18	25	
We		5	12	19	26	
Th		6	13	20	27	
Fr		7	14	21	28	
Sa	1	8	15	22	29	
Su	2	9	16	23	30	

August

Wk	31	32	33	34	35
Mo		7	14	21	28
Tu	1	8	15	22	29
We	2	9	16	23	30
Th	3	10	17	24	31
Fr	4	11	18	25	
Sa	5	12	19	26	
Su	6	13	20	27	

September

Wk	35	36	37	38	39
Mo		4	11	18	25
Tu		5	12	19	26
We		6	13	20	27
Th		7	14	21	28
Fr	1	8	15	22	29
Sa	2	9	16	23	30
Su	3	10	17	24	

October

Wk	39	40	41	42	43	44
Mo		2	9	16	23	30
Tu		3	10	17	24	31
We		4	11	18	25	
Th		5	12	19	26	
Fr		6	13	20	27	
Sa		7	14	21	28	
Su	1	8	15	22	29	

November

Wk	44	45	46	47	48
Mo		6	13	20	27
Tu		7	14	21	28
We	1	8	15	22	29
Th	2	9	16	23	30
Fr	3	10	17	24	
Sa	4	11	18	25	
Su	5	12	19	26	

December

Wk	48	49	50	51	52
Mo		4	11	18	25
Tu		5	12	19	26
We		6	13	20	27
Th		7	14	21	28
Fr	1	8	15	22	29
Sa	2	9	16	23	30
Su	3	10	17	24	31

December

2021	**WEEK 52**	Metal Ox Year 11. Lunar Month 24. - 26. Day

27 MO

己酉 Earth Rooster — *Earth* — 02:26 ☾ ♎
Roof — Harvest — 6 - 4 - 4

✲✲ ♥ € ⏻ ✶

⏻ ✸	00 - 01
∅ ♥	01 - 03
✶ € ♥	03 - 05
✸ ♥ ϟ	05 - 07
∅ ♥	07 - 09
	09 - 11
€	11 - 13
	13 - 15
⏻	15 - 17
∅ ✸ ♥	17 - 19
♥	19 - 21
€ ✈	21 - 23
♥ ⏻ ✸	23 - 00

䷶ 55-Overshadowing: Use your wealth with wisdom for your ambitions.

28 TU

庚戌 Metal Dog — *Metal* — 21:06 ♏
Room — Opening — 6 - 4 - 5

✲ ♥ ♥ ✈

♥	00 - 01
€ ♥ ✸	01 - 03
✸ ♥	03 - 05
∅ ✸ ♥	05 - 07
ϟ	07 - 09
	09 - 11
♥	11 - 13
♥ ♥	13 - 15
✸ ✈ €	15 - 17
♥	17 - 19
✸ ♥	19 - 21
✶ €	21 - 23
♥	23 - 00

䷝ 30-Brightness: Light your inner fire. Enlighten dark corners and unsettled affairs.

29 WE

辛亥 Metal Pig — *Metal* — ♏
Wall — Closing — 6 - 4 - 6

✲✲ ⏻ ✈ ✸

	00 - 01
	01 - 03
♥ ⏻ ♥	03 - 05
€ ✸ ♥	05 - 07
✸	07 - 09
∅ ✈ ϟ	09 - 11
⏻ ✸	11 - 13
✸ ♥	13 - 15
✶ € ♥	15 - 17
♥ ♥ €	17 - 19
∅ €	19 - 21
∅ ♥	21 - 23
	23 - 00

䷰ 49-Reforming: It is a convenient time for changes. Trust in your competence be persistent.

-00:52 EOT 0:00:00 CET/EST	Year *Earth* Month *Earth*	辛丑 Metal Ox Year 庚子 Metal Rat Month 辛丑 Winter Solstice

2021	**WEEK 52**	Metal Ox Year 11. Lunar Month 27. - 30. Day

December

30TH

壬子 Water Rat *Wood* 23:01 ♐
Astride Establishment 6 - 4 - 7

☆☆ ♥ ✸ ⏻ ✈ €

€ ✸	00 - 01
✸ ♥	01 - 03
✸ ✈	03 - 05
♥	05 - 07
♥	07 - 09
✶ € ⏻ ✸	09 - 11
✸ ϟ	11 - 13
∅ ♥ ✸	13 - 15
♥	15 - 17
♥	17 - 19
	19 - 21
♥ €	21 - 23
€ ✸	23 - 00

䷒ 19-Arriving: Seize the opportunity. Invest in your future.

31FR

癸丑 Water Ox *Wood* ♐
Rope Removal 6 - 4 - 8

★★ ♥ ♥ ∅ ✶

New Year's Eve

✸ € ♥	00 - 01
♥	01 - 03
✶ ✸	03 - 05
♥ ⏻	05 - 07
∅ ✸	07 - 09
⏻ ♥	09 - 11
♥	11 - 13
∅ € ♥ ϟ	13 - 15
	15 - 17
∅ ♥	17 - 19
∅ ♥	19 - 21
✸ ✈	21 - 23
✸ € ♥	23 - 00

䷨ 41-Decreasing: Affiliate honesty with self-restraint. Small things provoke big ones.

1SA

甲寅 Wood Tiger *Water* 22:56 ♑
Stomach Fulfillment 6 - 4 - 9

★ ♥ ⏻ ✸

New Year's Day

✸ ♥	00 - 01
	01 - 03
€ ✸ ♥	03 - 05
♥	05 - 07
€	07 - 09
∅ ♥	09 - 11
✸ ♥	11 - 13
⏻ ✸	13 - 15
∅ ✸ ♥ ✈ ϟ	15 - 17
€	17 - 19
♥	19 - 21
✶ ∅ € ♥ ♥	21 - 23
✸ ♥	23 - 00

䷻ 60-Regulating: Identify your limitations. Extend suffocating ones, establish wise ones.

2SU

乙卯 Wood Rabbit *Water* 18:35 ● ♑
Pleiades Balance 6 - 4 - 1

★★ ♥ ∅

♥	00 - 01
∅ ✸	01 - 03
	03 - 05
€ ✸	05 - 07
♥	07 - 09
✸ ♥ ✈	09 - 11
✸ ♥ €	11 - 13
✸ ♥	13 - 15
✶ € ⏻ ✸	15 - 17
♥ ϟ	17 - 19
∅ ♥ ♥	19 - 21
€ ♥	21 - 23
♥	23 - 00

䷼ 61-Mutually Trusting: Have an open mind and search for the true core. This arises understanding, adjacency and continuance.

-02:19 EOT 0:00:00 CET/EST	Year *Earth* Month *Earth*	辛丑 Metal Ox Year 庚子 Metal Rat Month 辛丑 Winter Solstice

January

2022	WEEK 1	Metal Ox Year 12. Lunar Month 1. - 3. Day

3 MO — 丙辰 Fire Dragon — *Earth* — 22:38 ♒
Net — Determination — 6 - 4 - 2

♥	00 - 01
	01 - 03
	03 - 05
	05 - 07
	07 - 09
	09 - 11
	11 - 13
	13 - 15
€ ♥	15 - 17
♥	17 - 19
	19 - 21
	21 - 23
♥	23 - 00

54-The Libidinal Addiction: Be true to your emotions and addiction but with retention.

4 TU — 丁巳 Fire Snake — *Earth* — ♒
Beak — Rigidity — 6 - 4 - 3

	00 - 01
♥	01 - 03
	03 - 05
	05 - 07
	07 - 09
	09 - 11
€	11 - 13
	13 - 15
	15 - 17
	17 - 19
€	19 - 21
	21 - 23
	23 - 00

38-Misunderstanding:
Remain true to yourself. Develop individual differences to constructive connections.

5 WE — 戊午 Earth Horse — *Fire* — ♒
Orion — Destruction / Rigidity — 6 - 4/3 - 4
until 09:15
★★ from 09:15
09:15 Slight Cold

€	00 - 01
	01 - 03
♥	03 - 05
	05 - 07
	07 - 09
	09 - 11
	11 - 13
♥	13 - 15
	15 - 17
	17 - 19
♥	19 - 21
	21 - 23
€	23 - 00

58-Pleasing: With an inner smile about yourself and the world you will win the hearts of other people and free your own.

-04:12 EOT 0:00:00 CET/EST	Year *Earth* Month *Earth*	辛丑 Metal Ox Year 庚子 Metal Rat Month 辛丑 Metal Ox Year 辛丑 Metal Ox Month Jan 05 09:15

2022	WEEK 1	Metal Ox Year 12. Lunar Month 4. - 7. Day

6TH

己未 Earth Goat — *Fire* — 00:14 ♓
Well — Destruction — 6 - 3 - 5

★★ ⚡ ♥ ✺ ∅

Three Kings' Day

♥⏻	00 - 01
∅✺♥⚡	01 - 03
€✺♥	03 - 05
♥	05 - 07
	07 - 09
✈	09 - 11
€♥	11 - 13
€✺	13 - 15
✈€⏻	15 - 17
∅✺♥	17 - 19
∅♥	19 - 21
♥	21 - 23
♥♥⏻	23 - 00

☰ 10-Treading: Show self-confidence and inner strength together with sereneness.

7FR

庚申 Metal Monkey — *Wood* — ♓
Ghosts — Danger — 6 - 3 - 6

★ € ⏻ ♥ ✈

✺♥	00 - 01
⏻	01 - 03
∅♥✈⚡	03 - 05
♥	05 - 07
€♥	07 - 09
✈∅€♥	09 - 11
♥	11 - 13
	13 - 15
€	15 - 17
€♥	17 - 19
♥	19 - 21
∅♥♥	21 - 23
✺♥	23 - 00

☷ 11-Prominence: Work together and complement one another. Everyone will profit.

8SA

辛酉 Metal Rooster — *Wood* — 05:32 ♈
Willow — Completion — 6 - 3 - 7

★★ ♥ ♥ ✺ € ⏻ ✈

✺♥	00 - 01
∅✺♥	01 - 03
✈€⏻✺	03 - 05
♥⚡	05 - 07
∅✺♥	07 - 09
	09 - 11
⏻€✺	11 - 13
✺	13 - 15
♥	15 - 17
∅♥€	17 - 19
♥♥	19 - 21
€✈	21 - 23
✺♥	23 - 00

☰ 26-Great Gains: Focus your strength. Go out and utilize your capabilities profitably.

9SU

壬戌 Water Dog — *Water* — 18:13 ☽ — ♈
Star — Harvest — 6 - 3 - 8

★★ ♥ € ✈

✺♥	00 - 01
∅€♥	01 - 03
✺♥	03 - 05
♥	05 - 07
⚡	07 - 09
⏻✺	09 - 11
✺♥♥	11 - 13
∅♥✺	13 - 15
✈€	15 - 17
♥♥	17 - 19
✺	19 - 21
✈	21 - 23
✺♥	23 - 00

☵ 5-Waiting: Be patient and pursue your goal, step by step.

-05:32 EOT 0:00:00 CET/EST	Year *Earth* Month *Earth*	辛丑 Metal Ox Year 辛丑 Metal Ox Month 辛丑 Slight Cold

January

2022	**WEEK 2**	Metal Ox Year 12. Lunar Month 8. - 10. Day

10 MO

癸亥 Water Pig — *Water* — 15:02 ♉
Bow — Opening — 6 - 3 - 9

☆☆ ♥♥ ♥ ✈

- ✷€ 00 - 01
- ✷ 01 - 03
- ♥♥ 03 - 05
- €⏻✷♥ 05 - 07
- ✷♥ 07 - 09
- ✈ϟ 09 - 11
- ♥ 11 - 13
- ♥ 13 - 15
- ✈€♥♥ 15 - 17
- ♥♥ 17 - 19
- ∅€ 19 - 21
- ∅✷♥ 21 - 23
- ✷€ 23 - 00

䷈ 9-Small Savings: Go for your ambition with small steps instead of great leaps.

11 TU

甲子 Wood Rat — *Metal* — ♉
Wings — Closing — 6 - 3 - 1

☆ ♥ ⏻ ✷

- €✷ 00 - 01
- ⏻✷♥ 01 - 03
- ✈€♥ 03 - 05
- ∅♥ 05 - 07
- ♥ 07 - 09
- ✈€♥ 09 - 11
- ✷♥ϟ 11 - 13
- ♥♥✷ 13 - 15
- ✷♥ 15 - 17
- ♥ 17 - 19
- ✷ 19 - 21
- ✷♥ 21 - 23
- €✷ 23 - 00

䷡ 34-Great Strength: Check your handling of power. Grandeur and justice belong together.

12 WE

乙丑 Wood Ox — *Metal* — ♉
Carriage — Establishment — 6 - 3 - 2

★★★ ♥ ⏻ ✈ ✷ €

- ⏻✷♥ 00 - 01
- ♥✷ 01 - 03
- ✈ 03 - 05
- ♥€ 05 - 07
- ∅ 07 - 09
- ✷♥ 09 - 11
- ✷♥♥ 11 - 13
- ∅€✷♥ϟ 13 - 15
- ⏻✷ 15 - 17
- ∅♥ 17 - 19
- ∅✷♥♥ 19 - 21
- ✷✈ 21 - 23
- ⏻✷♥ 23 - 00

䷍ 14-Great Reward: Use your capabilities and assets for common weal.

-07:14 EOT 0:00:00 CET/EST	Year *Earth* Month *Earth*	辛丑 Metal Ox Year 辛丑 Metal Ox Month 辛丑 Slight Cold

2022	**WEEK 2**	Metal Ox Year 12. Lunar Month 11. - 14. Day

January

13TH
丙寅 Fire Tiger — *Fire* — 03:24 ♊
Horn — Removal — 6 - 3 - 3
★★★

00 - 01
01 - 03
03 - 05
05 - 07
€ 07 - 09
€ 09 - 11
♥ 11 - 13
13 - 15
15 - 17
17 - 19
♥ 19 - 21
♥ 21 - 23
23 - 00

43-Severing: Stand up frankly for your own truth. Be determined but not offending.

14FR
丁卯 Fire Rabbit — *Fire* — ♊
Neck — Fulfillment — 6 - 3 - 4
♥ €

00 - 01
01 - 03
03 - 05
05 - 07
07 - 09
09 - 11
€ 11 - 13
♥ 13 - 15
15 - 17
17 - 19
♥ 19 - 21
♥ 21 - 23
23 - 00

44-Meeting: Examine a seductive offer with minuteness and hold off.

15SA
戊辰 Earth Dragon — *Wood* — 16:22 ♋
Base — Balance — 6 - 3 - 5

♥ 00 - 01
01 - 03
03 - 05
05 - 07
07 - 09
09 - 11
11 - 13
13 - 15
€♥ 15 - 17
♥ 17 - 19
19 - 21
21 - 23
♥ 23 - 00

28-Great Test: Do not blow your plans out of proportions. Be gentle and mind your balance.

16SU
己巳 Earth Snake — *Wood* — ♋
House — Determination — 6 - 3 - 6
★

00 - 01
♥ 01 - 03
03 - 05
05 - 07
07 - 09
09 - 11
€ 11 - 13
13 - 15
15 - 17
17 - 19
€ 19 - 21
21 - 23
23 - 00

50-The Caldron: Sort out material and spiritual ballast and create free space for new ideas.

-08:24 EOT 0:00:00 CET/EST	Year *Earth* Month *Earth*	辛丑 Metal Ox Year 辛丑 Metal Ox Month 辛丑 Slight Cold

2022	WEEK 3	Metal Ox Year 12. Lunar Month 15. - 17. Day

17 MO

庚午 Metal Horse — *Earth* — 23:51 ○ ♋

Heart — Rigidity — 6 - 3 - 7

★★★

	00 - 01
	01 - 03
♥	03 - 05
	05 - 07
	07 - 09
	09 - 11
	11 - 13
♥	13 - 15
€	15 - 17
	17 - 19
♥	19 - 21
	21 - 23
€	23 - 00

䷟ 32-Constancy: Take up a solid position without freezing.

18 TU

辛未 Metal Goat — *Earth* — 04:10 ♌

Tail — Destruction — 6 - 3 - 8

	00 - 01
	01 - 03
€	03 - 05
♥	05 - 07
	07 - 09
	09 - 11
♥	11 - 13
	13 - 15
	15 - 17
€	17 - 19
	19 - 21
♥	21 - 23
	23 - 00

䷸ 57-Penetrating: Get your goals clear and implement them, gentle but consequent.

19 WE

壬申 Water Monkey — *Metal* — ♌

Basket — Danger — 6 - 3 - 9

€

♥	00 - 01
	01 - 03
	03 - 05
	05 - 07
€ ♥	07 - 09
	09 - 11
	11 - 13
	13 - 15
	15 - 17
	17 - 19
	19 - 21
€	21 - 23
♥	23 - 00

䷯ 48-The Well: Develop your potentials and take good care of yourself.

-09:49 EOT 0:00:00 CET/EST	Year *Earth* Month *Earth*	辛丑 Metal Ox Year 辛丑 Metal Ox Month 辛丑 Slight Cold

2022	**WEEK 3**	Metal Ox Year 12. Lunar Month 18. - 21. Day

20TH

✹❤€	00 - 01
⌀✹♥	01 - 03
✗€	03 - 05
❤⏻✹⚡	05 - 07
⌀✹♥❤	07 - 09
⏻	09 - 11
€❤	11 - 13
	13 - 15
	15 - 17
⌀❤	17 - 19
♥❤	19 - 21
€✹✈	21 - 23
✹❤€	23 - 00

癸酉 Water Rooster *Metal* 14:04 ♍

Dipper Completion 6 - 3 - 1

★★★ ❤ ♥ ✹ € ⏻ ✈

02:40 Great Cold

18-Decaying: Do not be too good for humble work. Clear backlog.

21FR

❤	00 - 01
€♥✹	01 - 03
€♥❤	03 - 05
⌀♥	05 - 07
⚡	07 - 09
❤	09 - 11
✹♥	11 - 13
♥❤✹	13 - 15
✹✈€	15 - 17
♥❤	17 - 19
✹	19 - 21
✗€	21 - 23
❤	23 - 00

甲戌 Wood Dog *Fire* ♍

Ox Harvest 6 - 3 - 2

★★ ❤ € ✗

46-Rising: Rely on your intuition. Put your plans into action - now.

22SA

⏻✹	00 - 01
	01 - 03
❤♥	03 - 05
♥	05 - 07
❤	07 - 09
⌀✹✈⚡	09 - 11
✹	11 - 13
✹♥	13 - 15
✗€♥❤⏻	15 - 17
✹♥❤	17 - 19
⌀€❤	19 - 21
⌀♥	21 - 23
⏻✹	23 - 00

乙亥 Wood Pig *Fire* 21:57 ♎

Maiden Opening 6 - 3 - 3

★★★ ❤ ♥ ✈ ✹

6-Litigating:
Be honest but not stubborn or impolite. Solve a conflict with empathy and compromising.

23SU

€✹	00 - 01
♥	01 - 03
✈	03 - 05
⌀♥❤	05 - 07
✹♥	07 - 09
✗✹	09 - 11
❤⚡	11 - 13
⌀♥❤	13 - 15
✹♥❤	15 - 17
❤⏻	17 - 19
	19 - 21
♥⏻✹	21 - 23
€✹	23 - 00

丙子 Fire Rat *Water* ♎

Void Closing 6 - 3 - 4

✗ ❤ ♥ ⏻ ✹

47-Confining: Benefit from your problems for your progress but do not talk about it.

-10:46 EOT 0:00:00 CET/EST	Year *Earth* Month *Earth*	辛丑 Metal Ox Year 辛丑 Metal Ox Month 辛丑 Great Cold Jan 20 02:40

January

2022	WEEK 4	Metal Ox Year 12. Lunar Month 22. - 24. Day

24 MO

丁丑 Fire Ox — *Water* — ♎
Roof — Establishment — 6 - 3 - 5

✫✫ ♥ ⏻ ✈ ₠

♥	00 - 01
♥✸	01 - 03
✶✸₩	03 - 05
✸₩	05 - 07
⌀₩	07 - 09
♥	09 - 11
♥€	11 - 13
⌀₠♥ϟ	13 - 15
✸	15 - 17
♥	17 - 19
⌀♥	19 - 21
✈⏻✸	21 - 23
♥₩	23 - 00

䷿ 64-Not Yet Accomplished: Specify precisely what you want to start but finish it definitely.

25 TU

戊寅 Earth Tiger — *Earth* — 13:42 ☾ 03:47 ♏
Room — Removal — 6 - 3 - 6

★★ ₩ ₠ ⌀ ✶

✸₩	00 - 01
₩	01 - 03
✸	03 - 05
♥✸	05 - 07
€₩	07 - 09
⌀♥₩€	09 - 11
♥	11 - 13
⏻✸	13 - 15
⌀✸♥✈ϟ	15 - 17
₠✸	17 - 19
✸♥	19 - 21
✶⌀₠✸♥	21 - 23
✸₩	23 - 00

䷧ 40-Separating: Disengage yourself from dead weight and return to your roots. Complete necessary objectives immediately.

26 WE

己卯 Earth Rabbit — *Earth* — ♏
Wall — Fulfillment — 6 - 3 - 7

✫✫ ♥ € ✈ ₩

♥✸₩	00 - 01
⌀	01 - 03
✸₩	03 - 05
✸	05 - 07
♥₩	07 - 09
♥✈	09 - 11
₩€	11 - 13
♥	13 - 15
✶₠⏻	15 - 17
✸₩ϟ	17 - 19
⌀♥₩	19 - 21
₠♥	21 - 23
♥✸	23 - 00

䷺ 59-Dispersing: Break deadlocked structures with changes and shared joy.

-11:51 EOT 0:00:00 CET/EST	Year *Earth* Month *Earth*	辛丑 Metal Ox Year 辛丑 Metal Ox Month 辛丑 Great Cold

2022	WEEK 4	Metal Ox Year 12. Lunar Month 25. - 28. Day

27TH 庚辰 Metal Dragon — *Metal* — 07:27 ♐
Astride — Balance — 6 - 3 - 8
★★

♥	00 - 01
01 - 03
03 - 05
05 - 07
07 - 09
09 - 11
11 - 13
13 - 15
15 - 17
17 - 19
19 - 21
21 - 23
♥ 23 - 00

29-Cavern: Be truly and sincere to yourself. Overcome obstacles peacefully.

28FR 辛巳 Metal Snake — *Metal* — ♐
Rope — Determination — 6 - 3 - 9
★

00 - 01, ♥ 01 - 03, 03 - 05, 05 - 07, 07 - 09, 09 - 11, 11 - 13, 13 - 15, 15 - 17, 17 - 19, € 19 - 21, 21 - 23, 23 - 00

4-Ignorance: Be enthusiastic and open minded but rely on your experience.

29SA 壬午 Water Horse — *Wood* — 09:04 ♑
Stomach — Rigidity — 6 - 3 - 1
★★★

00 - 01, 01 - 03, 03 - 05, 05 - 07, 07 - 09, 09 - 11, 11 - 13, 13 - 15, 15 - 17, 17 - 19, ♥ 19 - 21, 21 - 23, 23 - 00

33-Retiring: A retreat in the right moment saves your dignity. Be insistent.

30SU 癸未 Water Goat — *Wood* — ♑
Pleiades — Destruction — 6 - 3 - 2
★★★

00 - 01, 01 - 03, € 03 - 05, 05 - 07, 07 - 09, 09 - 11, 11 - 13, 13 - 15, 15 - 17, 17 - 19, 19 - 21, 21 - 23, 23 - 00

31-Influencing:
Reconcile your ambitions and your needs. Use the natural power of attraction of all things.

-12:32 EOT 0:00:00 CET/EST	Year *Earth* Month *Earth*	辛丑 Metal Ox Year 辛丑 Metal Ox Month 辛丑 Great Cold

2022	WEEK 5	Metal Ox Year 12. Lunar Month 29. Day Water Tiger Year 1. Lunar Month 1. - 2. Day
♥ 00 - 01 01 - 03 03 - 05 05 - 07 €♥ 07 - 09 09 - 11 11 - 13 13 - 15 15 - 17 17 - 19 19 - 21 21 - 23 ♥ 23 - 00	31 MO ★	甲申 Wood Monkey *Water* 09:35 ♒ Net Danger 6 - 3 - 3 € 56-Traveling: Scoop from your inner source, be attentive and start for new shore.
00 - 01 ♥ 01 - 03 03 - 05 € 05 - 07 ♥ 07 - 09 09 - 11 € 11 - 13 13 - 15 15 - 17 17 - 19 19 - 21 21 - 23 23 - 00	1 TU ★★★	乙酉 Wood Rooster *Water* 05:49 ● ♒ Beak Completion 6 - 3 - 4 ♥ € Chinese New Year 62-Small Testing: Concentrate on the details and complete them with accuracy.
00 - 01 01 - 03 ♥ 03 - 05 ♥ 05 - 07 07 - 09 € 09 - 11 ♥ 11 - 13 13 - 15 € 15 - 17 17 - 19 19 - 21 21 - 23 23 - 00	2 WE	丙戌 Fire Dog *Earth* 10:50 ♓ Orion Harvest 6 - 3 - 5 € 53-Gradually Progressing: Achieve your plans, patient and with integrity.
-13:15 EOT 0:00:00 CET/EST	Year *Earth* Month *Earth*	辛丑 Metal Ox Year 辛丑 Metal Ox Month 辛丑 Great Cold

2022	**WEEK 5**	Water Tiger Year 1. Lunar Month 3. - 6. Day

February

00 - 01 01 - 03 ✷♥ 03 - 05 €✷♥ 05 - 07 07 - 09 ∅✈⚡ 09 - 11 ✷€♥ 11 - 13 ✷♥ 13 - 15 ✈€♥♥ 15 - 17 ♥♥⏻✷ 17 - 19 ∅€ 19 - 21 ♥✷ 21 - 23 ♥ 23 - 00	3TH ★★ ★	丁亥 Fire Pig *Earth* ♓ Well Opening / Harvest 6/5 - 3/2 - 6 ♥ ♥ ✈ until 20:51 ♥ ✷ ⏻ ✈ from 20:51 20:51 Coming of Spring ䷦ 39-Obstructing: Do not bash your head against a wall. Retreat, bethink and talk to friends.
€ 00 - 01 ⏻♥♥ 01 - 03 ✈ 03 - 05 ∅♥✷ 05 - 07 ♥♥ 07 - 09 ✈ 09 - 11 ✷♥⚡ 11 - 13 ♥♥ 13 - 15 ♥ 15 - 17 ♥ 17 - 19 ✷ 19 - 21 ✷♥♥ 21 - 23 € 23 - 00	4FR ★	戊子 Earth Rat *Fire* 14:50 ♈ Ghosts Opening 5 - 2 - 7 ♥ € ✈ ䷳ 52-Stopping: Make peace with your core and do not get disturbed by emotions.
⏻✷♥♥ 00 - 01 ♥✷ 01 - 03 ✈✷♥ 03 - 05 ♥ 05 - 07 ∅♥ 07 - 09 ♥ 09 - 11 ✷♥♥€ 11 - 13 ∅€✷♥⚡ 13 - 15 ⏻ 15 - 17 ∅✷♥ 17 - 19 ∅♥♥ 19 - 21 ✈ 21 - 23 ⏻✷♥ 23 - 00	5SA ☆☆	己丑 Earth Ox *Fire* ♈ Willow Closing 5 - 2 - 8 ✷ ䷎ 15-Modesty: Be modest but not humble or self-deprecating. Engage in common cause.
♥ 00 - 01 ✷ 01 - 03 ✷ 03 - 05 ♥ 05 - 07 € 07 - 09 ∅♥♥ 09 - 11 ♥ 11 - 13 ⏻ 13 - 15 ∅✷♥✈€⚡ 15 - 17 €♥ 17 - 19 ♥♥ 19 - 21 ✈∅€♥♥ 21 - 23 ♥ 23 - 00	6SU ☆☆	庚寅 Metal Tiger *Wood* 22:57 ♉ Star Establishment 5 - 2 - 9 ♥ ⏻ ✈ € ䷋ 12-Adversity: Keep your balance and listen to your heart. Savor everyday commodities.
-13:39 EOT 0:00:00 CET/EST	Year *Earth* Month *Earth*	辛丑 Metal Ox Year 辛丑 Metal Ox Month 壬寅 Water Tiger Year 壬寅 Water Tiger Month Feb 03 20:51

February

2022	**WEEK 6**	Water Tiger Year 1. Lunar Month 7. - 9. Day

7 MO

辛卯 Metal Rabbit *Wood* ♉
Bow Removal 5 - 2 - 1

★ ❣ ⌀ ✈̸

⌀❥	00 - 01
⌀	01 - 03
⏻ ✹	03 - 05
✹	05 - 07
✸❥❣	07 - 09
❥✈	09 - 11
❣⏻€	11 - 13
✸♥	13 - 15
✈̸€̸❣	15 - 17
❣€ϟ	17 - 19
⌀♥	19 - 21
€̸♥	21 - 23
⌀❥	23 - 00

䷬ 45-Gathering: Personal sacrifices foster your personal up growth.

8 TU

壬辰 Water Dragon *Water* 13:51 ☽ ♉
Wings Fulfillment 5 - 2 - 2

★ ♥ € ✈ ✸

♥	00 - 01
€̸❣✹	01 - 03
✸✈	03 - 05
❥❣	05 - 07
⌀❥	07 - 09
✈̸€̸⏻✹	09 - 11
✸	11 - 13
⌀❥❣	13 - 15
€♥	15 - 17
♥	17 - 19
ϟ	19 - 21
€	21 - 23
♥	23 - 00

䷢ 35-Promoting: Be upright, noble and generous. The lust for life evolves from good deeds.

9 WE

癸巳 Water Snake *Water* 10:41 ♊
Carriage Balance 5 - 2 - 3

☆̸☆̸ ❥ ✸ ⌀

✸€	00 - 01
✸♥	01 - 03
✈̸⌀€̸❥❣	03 - 05
€̸❣⏻✹	05 - 07
⌀✹❣	07 - 09
	09 - 11
✸❣	11 - 13
✸	13 - 15
⌀❣	15 - 17
	17 - 19
€	19 - 21
✸✈ϟ	21 - 23
✸€	23 - 00

䷏ 16-Satisfying: Pass your enthusiasm to others. Together you will succeed faster.

-13:59 EOT 0:00:00 CET/EST	Year *Metal* Month *Metal*	壬寅 Water Tiger Year 壬寅 Water Tiger Month 壬寅 Coming of Spring

2022	**WEEK 6**	Water Tiger Year 1. Lunar Month 10. - 13. Day

February

10TH

甲午 Wood Horse — *Metal* — ♊
Horn — Determination — 5 - 2 - 4

★★★

00 - 01
01 - 03
03 - 05
05 - 07
07 - 09
09 - 11
11 - 13
13 - 15
15 - 17
17 - 19
19 - 21
21 - 23
23 - 00

20-Observing: Take the time to take personal stock as a basis for your spiritual growth.

11FR

乙未 Wood Goat — *Metal* — 23:43 ♋
Neck — Rigidity — 5 - 2 - 5

00 - 01
01 - 03
03 - 05
05 - 07
07 - 09
09 - 11
11 - 13
13 - 15
15 - 17
17 - 19
19 - 21
21 - 23
23 - 00

8-Alliance: Do not hesitate to act jointly.

12SA

丙申 Fire Monkey — *Fire* — ♋
Base — Destruction — 5 - 2 - 6

00 - 01
01 - 03
03 - 05
05 - 07
07 - 09
09 - 11
11 - 13
13 - 15
15 - 17
17 - 19
19 - 21
21 - 23
23 - 00

23-Stripping: Dark clouds are rising. Retreat and bethink yourself.

13SU

丁酉 Fire Rooster — *Fire* — ♋
House — Danger — 5 - 2 - 7

★★★

00 - 01
01 - 03
03 - 05
05 - 07
07 - 09
09 - 11
11 - 13
13 - 15
15 - 17
17 - 19
19 - 21
21 - 23
23 - 00

24-Returning: Something re-enters your life. Clarify your ambitions to get a good start.

-14:06 EOT 0:00:00 CET/EST	Year *Metal* Month *Metal*	壬寅 Water Tiger Year 壬寅 Water Tiger Month 壬寅 Coming of Spring

2022	**WEEK 7**	Water Tiger Year 1. Lunar Month 14. - 16. Day
✸❤ 00 - 01 €♥❤ 01 - 03 ♥ 03 - 05 ∅✸♥ 05 - 07 ✸❤ϟ 07 - 09 ✸€ 09 - 11 ♥ 11 - 13 ♥❤✸ 13 - 15 ✈€ 15 - 17 ♥❤ 17 - 19 19 - 21 ✈€✸❤ 21 - 23 ✸❤ 23 - 00	14 MO ☆☆ϟ	戊戌 Earth Dog *Wood* 11:32 ♌ Heart Completion 5 - 2 - 8 ❤ ♥ ✸ ⏻ ✈ Valentine's Day ☶☳ 27-Jaws: Take care of your corporal and mental nourishment.
⏻✸❤ 00 - 01 01 - 03 ✸♥ 03 - 05 €♥ 05 - 07 ✸ 07 - 09 ∅✸✈ϟ 09 - 11 € 11 - 13 ♥ 13 - 15 ✈€♥❤⏻ 15 - 17 ✸♥❤ 17 - 19 ∅€❤ 19 - 21 ∅♥ 21 - 23 ⏻✸ 23 - 00	15 TU ★	己亥 Earth Pig *Wood* ♌ Tail Harvest 5 - 2 - 9 ♥ ⏻ ✈ ☵☳ 3-Accumulating: The start is difficult. Be patient and accept help. You will be successful.
€✸ 00 - 01 ⏻✸♥ 01 - 03 ✈ 03 - 05 ∅♥ 05 - 07 ✸♥ 07 - 09 ✈€✸ 09 - 11 ❤ϟ 11 - 13 ♥❤ 13 - 15 ✸€♥ 15 - 17 17 - 19 ❤ 19 - 21 ♥ 21 - 23 €✸ 23 - 00	16 WE ★	庚子 Metal Rat *Earth* 16:59 ○ 20:54 ♍ Basket Opening 5 - 2 - 1 ♥ € ✈ ☴☳ 42-Increasing: Use your abilities for common welfare. Learn from mistakes.
-14:04 EOT 0:00:00 CET/EST	Year *Metal* Month *Metal*	壬寅 Water Tiger Year 壬寅 Water Tiger Month 壬寅 Coming of Spring

2022	**WEEK 7**	Water Tiger Year 1. Lunar Month 17. - 20. Day

17TH

辛丑 Metal Ox — *Earth* — ♍
Dipper — Closing — 5 - 2 - 2

☆ ✹

♥	00 - 01
♥✹	01 - 03
✶⏻✹	03 - 05
♥♥	05 - 07
⌀✹♥♥	07 - 09
♥	09 - 11
♥♥♥⏻✹	11 - 13
⌀€✹♥ϟ	13 - 15
♥♥	15 - 17
⌀€♥	17 - 19
⌀♥	19 - 21
✈	21 - 23
♥	23 - 00

☳ 51-Startling:
A change is imminent. Keep your calmness and humor, everything will turn to good account.

18FR

壬寅 Water Tiger — *Metal* — ♍
Ox — Establishment — 5 - 2 - 3

★ ♥ ⏻ ✈ €
16:44 Rain Water

♥♥	00 - 01
⌀✹	01 - 03
	03 - 05
♥⏻	05 - 07
✹€	07 - 09
♥♥♥	09 - 11
✹♥♥♥	11 - 13
✹♥♥	13 - 15
⌀♥✈ϟ	15 - 17
€	17 - 19
♥	19 - 21
✶⌀♥♥♥	21 - 23
♥♥	23 - 00

☲ 21-Gnawing And Chewing: Conquer difficulties with discipline and justice.

19SA

癸卯 Water Rabbit — *Metal* — 03:55 ♎
Maiden — Removal — 5 - 2 - 4

★ ♥♥ ⌀ ✶

⌀✹♥€	00 - 01
⌀✹	01 - 03
	03 - 05
⏻✹	05 - 07
♥	07 - 09
♥✈⏻	09 - 11
€	11 - 13
♥	13 - 15
✶€	15 - 17
♥♥ϟ	17 - 19
⌀♥	19 - 21
€✹♥	21 - 23
⌀✹♥€	23 - 00

☱ 17-Following: Learn everything from the scratch and accept advice. This is the basis of authority and recognition.

20SU

甲辰 Wood Dragon — *Fire* — ♎
Void — Fulfillment — 5 - 2 - 5

☆☆ ♥ € ✈ ✹

♥	00 - 01
€♥♥⏻✹	01 - 03
✹✈€♥♥	03 - 05
⌀✹♥♥♥	05 - 07
⌀♥	07 - 09
✶€♥♥	09 - 11
✹♥♥	11 - 13
♥✹	13 - 15
✹€♥	15 - 17
♥	17 - 19
ϟ	19 - 21
	21 - 23
♥	23 - 00

☰ 25-Without Wrongdoing: Follow your intuition without calculating intention.

-13:55 EOT 0:00:00 CET/EST	Year *Metal* Month *Metal*	壬寅 Water Tiger Year 壬寅 Water Tiger Month 壬寅 Rain Water Feb 18 16:44

2022	**WEEK 8**	Water Tiger Year 1. Lunar Month 21. - 23. Day

21 MO

乙巳 Wood Snake *Fire* 09:15 ♏

Roof Balance 5 - 2 - 6

✩✩ ❥ ✹ ∅

⏻ ✸	00 - 01
♥	01 - 03
✗✈ ∅ ∅€ ✹ ❥ ♥♥	03 - 05
✹ ♥♥	05 - 07
∅ ♥♥	07 - 09
∅	09 - 11
✹	11 - 13
✹	13 - 15
♥♥ ✸	15 - 17
	17 - 19
€ ♥♥	19 - 21
✈ ϟ	21 - 23
⏻ ✸	23 - 00

䷣ 36-Brightness Wounded: Hide your light under a bushel and persecute your aim.

22 TU

丙午 Fire Horse *Water* ♏

Room Determination 5 - 2 - 7

★★★ ♥♥ ⏻

♥♥ € ✸ ϟ	00 - 01
∅ ❥ ♥♥	01 - 03
✹ ♥	03 - 05
✹	05 - 07
✹	07 - 09
✹	09 - 11
∅ ❥	11 - 13
∅ ♥	13 - 15
✈ ♥♥	15 - 17
⏻ ✸	17 - 19
♥	19 - 21
✗✈ ∅€ ❥ ⏻ ✸	21 - 23
♥♥ € ✸ ϟ	23 - 00

䷕ 22-Adorning: Design everything functional and beautiful because beauty fosters function.

23 WE

丁未 Fire Goat *Water* 22:34 ☾ 13:25 ♐

Wall Rigidity 5 - 2 - 8

★ ✸ ⏻ ✗✈

❥ ♥♥	00 - 01
∅ ❥ ϟ	01 - 03
✹ € ♥♥	03 - 05
✹ ♥	05 - 07
	07 - 09
✈	09 - 11
€ ♥ ♥♥	11 - 13
∅€ ✸	13 - 15
✗✈ ∅€	15 - 17
♥♥ ✸	17 - 19
∅ ❥ ♥♥	19 - 21
⏻ ✸ ♥	21 - 23
❥	23 - 00

䷾ 63-Already Accomplished: An end is achieved. Finish accurately and prepare for the next begin.

-13:33 EOT 0:00:00 CET/EST	Year *Metal* Month *Metal*	壬寅 Water Tiger Year 壬寅 Water Tiger Month 壬寅 Rain Water

2022	WEEK 8	Water Tiger Year 1. Lunar Month 24. - 27. Day

February

24TH

戊申 Earth Monkey — *Earth* — ♐

Astride — Destruction — 5 - 2 - 9

00 - 01
01 - 03
03 - 05
05 - 07
07 - 09
09 - 11
11 - 13
13 - 15
15 - 17
17 - 19
19 - 21
21 - 23
23 - 00

37-Family: Be reliable and consolidate the output as a solid platform for further developments.

25FR

己酉 Earth Rooster — *Earth* — 16:28 ♑

Rope — Danger — 5 - 2 - 1

00 - 01
01 - 03
03 - 05
05 - 07
07 - 09
09 - 11
11 - 13
13 - 15
15 - 17
17 - 19
19 - 21
21 - 23
23 - 00

55-Overshadowing: Use your wealth with wisdom for your ambitions.

26SA

庚戌 Metal Dog — *Metal* — ♑

Stomach — Completion — 5 - 2 - 2

00 - 01
01 - 03
03 - 05
05 - 07
07 - 09
09 - 11
11 - 13
13 - 15
15 - 17
17 - 19
19 - 21
21 - 23
23 - 00

30-Brightness: Light your inner fire. Enlighten dark corners and unsettled affairs.

27SU

辛亥 Metal Pig — *Metal* — 18:36 ♒

Pleiades — Harvest — 5 - 2 - 3

00 - 01
01 - 03
03 - 05
05 - 07
07 - 09
09 - 11
11 - 13
13 - 15
15 - 17
17 - 19
19 - 21
21 - 23
23 - 00

49-Reforming: It is a convenient time for changes. Trust in your competence be persistent.

-13:09 EOT 0:00:00 CET/EST	Year *Metal* Month *Metal*	壬寅 Water Tiger Year 壬寅 Water Tiger Month 壬寅 Rain Water

2022	WEEK 9	Water Tiger Year 1. Lunar Month 28. - 30. Day

28 MO

壬子 Water Rat — *Wood* — ♒
Net — Opening — 5 - 2 - 4

★ ♥ € ✈
Rose Monday

€✹	00 - 01
✹♥	01 - 03
✹✈	03 - 05
♥	05 - 07
♥	07 - 09
✈€⏻✹	09 - 11
✹⚡	11 - 13
∅♥✹	13 - 15
♥	15 - 17
♥	17 - 19
	19 - 21
♥€	21 - 23
€✹	23 - 00

䷒ 19-Arriving: Seize the opportunity. Invest in your future.

1 TU

癸丑 Water Ox — *Wood* — 20:47 ♓
Beak — Closing — 5 - 2 - 5

✩✩ ✹

✹€♥	00 - 01
♥	01 - 03
✈✹	03 - 05
♥⏻	05 - 07
∅✹	07 - 09
⏻♥	09 - 11
♥	11 - 13
∅€♥⚡	13 - 15
	15 - 17
∅♥	17 - 19
∅♥	19 - 21
✹✈	21 - 23
✹€♥	23 - 00

䷨ 41-Decreasing: Affiliate honesty with self-restraint. Small things provoke big ones.

2 WE

甲寅 Wood Tiger — *Water* — 17:38 ● — ♓
Orion — Establishment — 5 - 2 - 6

✩✩ ♥ ⏻ ✈ €
Ash Wednesday

✹♥	00 - 01
	01 - 03
€✹♥	03 - 05
♥	05 - 07
€	07 - 09
∅♥	09 - 11
✹♥	11 - 13
⏻✹	13 - 15
∅✹♥✈⚡	15 - 17
€	17 - 19
♥	19 - 21
✈∅€♥♥	21 - 23
✹♥	23 - 00

䷻ 60-Regulating: Identify your limitations. Extend suffocating ones, establish wise ones.

-12:30 EOT 0:00:00 CET/EST	Year *Metal* Month *Metal*	壬寅 Water Tiger Year 壬寅 Water Tiger Month 壬寅 Rain Water

2022	**WEEK 9**	Water Tiger Year 2. Lunar Month 1. - 4. Day

3 TH

乙卯 Wood Rabbit — *Water* — ♓

Well — Removal — 5 - 2 - 7

★ ♥ ∅ ✈

♥	00 - 01
∅✸	01 - 03
	03 - 05
€✸	05 - 07
♥	07 - 09
✸♥✈	09 - 11
✸♥€	11 - 13
✸♥	13 - 15
✈€⏻✸	15 - 17
♥ϟ	17 - 19
∅♥♥	19 - 21
€♥	21 - 23
♥	23 - 00

☴☱ 61-Mutually Trusting: Have an open mind and search for the true core. This arises understanding, adjacency and continuance.

4 FR

丙辰 Fire Dragon — *Earth* — 00:41 ♈

Ghosts — Fulfillment — 5 - 2 - 8

★ ♥ € ⏻ ✈

♥	00 - 01
€✸♥	01 - 03
✈	03 - 05
∅♥	05 - 07
∅✸♥	07 - 09
✈✸	09 - 11
♥	11 - 13
∅♥	13 - 15
€♥♥	15 - 17
⏻✸♥	17 - 19
ϟ	19 - 21
⏻✸	21 - 23
♥	23 - 00

☳☱ 54-The Libidinal Addiction: Be true to your emotions and addiction but with retention.

5 SA

丁巳 Fire Snake — *Earth* — ♈

Willow — Balance / Fulfillment — 5 - 2/1 - 9

✩ ♥ — until 14:44

★★ ♥ € ⏻ ✈ ✸ — from 14:44

14:44 Waking of Worms

✸	00 - 01
✸♥	01 - 03
✈∅€✸♥	03 - 05
€✸♥	05 - 07
∅	07 - 09
∅✸	09 - 11
€♥	11 - 13
	13 - 15
∅♥	15 - 17
⏻✸	17 - 19
€	19 - 21
✈⏻✸ϟ	21 - 23
✸♥	23 - 00

☲☱ 38-Misunderstanding:
Remain true to yourself. Develop individual differences to constructive connections.

6 SU

戊午 Earth Horse — *Fire* — 07:52 ♉

Star — Balance — 5 - 1 - 1

✩ ∅

✸♥€ϟ	00 - 01
♥	01 - 03
♥	03 - 05
♥✸	05 - 07
♥	07 - 09
	09 - 11
∅♥	11 - 13
✸♥	13 - 15
✈	15 - 17
	17 - 19
✸♥	19 - 21
✈€✸♥♥	21 - 23
✸♥€ϟ	23 - 00

☱☱ 58-Pleasing: With an inner smile about yourself and the world you will win the hearts of other people and free your own.

-11:55 EOT 0:00:00 CET/EST	Year *Metal* Month *Metal*	壬寅 Water Tiger Year 壬寅 Water Tiger Month 壬寅 Water Tiger Year 壬寅 Water Rabbit Month Mar 05 14:44

2022	WEEK 10	Water Tiger Year 2. Lunar Month 5. - 7. Day

7 MO

己未 Earth Goat — *Fire* — ♉
Bow — Determination — 5 - 1 - 2

✡̸ ❤

♥⏻	00 - 01
∅✹♥ϟ	01 - 03
€✹❤	03 - 05
♥	05 - 07
	07 - 09
✈	09 - 11
€♥	11 - 13
€̸✹	13 - 15
✈̸€̸⏻	15 - 17
∅✹❤	17 - 19
∅♥	19 - 21
♥	21 - 23
♥❤⏻	23 - 00

☰ 10-Treading: Show self-confidence and inner strength together with sereneness.

8 TU

庚申 Metal Monkey — *Wood* — 18:41 ♊
Wings — Rigidity — 5 - 1 - 3

✡̸✡̸ϟ ✹⏻ ❤€̸

✹♥	00 - 01
⏻	01 - 03
∅♥✈ϟ	03 - 05
♥	05 - 07
€♥	07 - 09
✈̸∅€̸❤	09 - 11
❤	11 - 13
	13 - 15
€	15 - 17
€̸❤	17 - 19
❤	19 - 21
∅♥❤	21 - 23
✹♥	23 - 00

☰ 11-Prominence: Work together and complement one another. Everyone will profit.

9 WE

辛酉 Metal Rooster — *Wood* — ♊
Carriage — Destruction — 5 - 1 - 4

✡̸✡̸ϟ ❤♥✹

✹❤	00 - 01
∅✹♥	01 - 03
✈̸€̸⏻✹	03 - 05
❤ϟ	05 - 07
∅✹♥	07 - 09
	09 - 11
⏻€✹	11 - 13
✹	13 - 15
❤	15 - 17
∅♥€	17 - 19
♥❤	19 - 21
€̸✈	21 - 23
✹❤	23 - 00

☰ 26-Great Gains: Focus your strength. Go out and utilize your capabilities profitably.

-11:02 EOT 0:00:00 CET/EST	Year *Metal* Month *Metal*	壬寅 Water Tiger Year 癸卯 Water Rabbit Month 壬寅 Waking of Worms

2022	WEEK **10**	Water Tiger Year	2. Lunar Month	8. - 11. Day

10TH

壬戌 Water Dog | *Water* | 10:46 ☽ | ♊
Horn | Danger | 5 - 1 - 5

☆̸☆̸ ♥ ❣̸ ✹̸ ⏻̸ ✈̸

✹̸❣̸	00 - 01
⏻̸€̸♥̸	01 - 03
✹̸♥	03 - 05
♥	05 - 07
ϟ	07 - 09
⏻✹	09 - 11
✹̸♥❣	11 - 13
⏻̸♥̸✹	13 - 15
✈€	15 - 17
♥̸❣̸	17 - 19
✹	19 - 21
✈̸	21 - 23
✹̸❣̸	23 - 00

䷄ 5-Waiting: Be patient and pursue your goal, step by step.

11FR

癸亥 Water Pig | *Water* | 07:34 ♋
Neck | Completion | 5 - 1 - 6

★★★ ♥ ✹ ⏻

✹̸€	00 - 01
✹̸	01 - 03
❣̸♥	03 - 05
€̸⏻✹♥	05 - 07
✹❣	07 - 09
✈ϟ	09 - 11
❣	11 - 13
♥	13 - 15
✈̸€̸♥̸❣̸	15 - 17
♥̸❣̸	17 - 19
⏻̸€	19 - 21
⏻̸✹̸♥̸	21 - 23
✹̸€	23 - 00

䷈ 9-Small Savings: Go for your ambition with small steps instead of great leaps.

12SA

甲子 Wood Rat | *Metal* | ♋
Base | Harvest | 5 - 1 - 7

☆̸☆̸ ✹ € ✈̸

€✹	00 - 01
⏻✹♥	01 - 03
✈€❣	03 - 05
⏻̸♥̸	05 - 07
♥	07 - 09
✈̸€̸❣	09 - 11
✹̸❣̸ϟ	11 - 13
♥̸❣̸✹	13 - 15
✹̸♥	15 - 17
❣̸	17 - 19
✹̸	19 - 21
✹̸♥̸	21 - 23
€✹	23 - 00

䷡ 34-Great Strength: Check your handling of power. Grandeur and justice belong together.

13SU

乙丑 Wood Ox | *Metal* | 19:46 ♌
House | Opening | 5 - 1 - 8

☆̸☆̸ ❣ ♥ ✈ ⏻̸

02:00 EST Clock changed to 03:00 EDT

⏻✹♥	00 - 01
♥̸✹	01 - 03
✈̸	03 - 05
❣̸€	05 - 07
⏻̸	07 - 09
✹̸♥	09 - 11
✹̸♥̸❣̸	11 - 13
⏻̸€̸✹̸♥̸ϟ	13 - 15
⏻✹	15 - 17
⏻̸♥	17 - 19
⏻̸✹̸♥̸❣	19 - 21
✹̸✈	21 - 23
⏻✹♥	23 - 00

䷍ 14-Great Reward: Use your capabilities and assets for common weal.

-10:17 EOT 0:00:00 CET/EST	Year *Metal* Month *Metal*	壬寅 Water Tiger Year 癸卯 Water Rabbit Month 壬寅 Waking of Worms

2022	WEEK 11	Water Tiger Year 2. Lunar Month 12. - 14. Day

14 MO

丙寅 Fire Tiger — *Fire* — ♌
Heart — Closing — 5 - 1 - 9

★ ⏻ ✸

❦✹	00 - 01
∅	01 - 03
✹	03 - 05
❥❦	05 - 07
✸€	07 - 09
∅✸❥❦€	09 - 11
♥	11 - 13
	13 - 15
∅❥✈❦ϟ	15 - 17
₠⏻✹	17 - 19
✸♥	19 - 21
✗₠❦♥	21 - 23
❦✹	23 - 00

䷪ 43-Severing: Stand up frankly for your own truth. Be determined but not offending.

15 TU

丁卯 Fire Rabbit — *Fire* — ♌
Tail — Establishment — 5 - 1 - 1

★ ❦♥⏻✈ ✸₠

∅❥	00 - 01
∅	01 - 03
✸❦	03 - 05
	05 - 07
❥❦	07 - 09
❥✈	09 - 11
€	11 - 13
♥	13 - 15
✗₠	15 - 17
❦⏻✹ϟ	17 - 19
∅✸♥	19 - 21
₠⏻♥	21 - 23
∅❥❦	23 - 00

䷫ 44-Meeting: Examine a seductive offer with minuteness and hold off.

16 WE

戊辰 Earth Dragon — *Wood* — 05:15 ♍
Basket — Removal — 5 - 1 - 2

★ ❥✸∅✗

✸♥	00 - 01
₠⏻	01 - 03
✈	03 - 05
∅❥❦✹	05 - 07
∅❥❦	07 - 09
✗	09 - 11
❦	11 - 13
❥✹	13 - 15
€♥	15 - 17
♥	17 - 19
✸ϟ	19 - 21
✸❦	21 - 23
✸♥	23 - 00

䷛ 28-Great Test: Do not blow your plans out of proportions. Be gentle and mind your balance.

-09:14 EOT 1:00:00 EDT	Year *Metal* Month *Metal*	壬寅 Water Tiger Year 癸卯 Water Rabbit Month 壬寅 Waking of Worms

2022	**WEEK 11**	Water Tiger Year 2. Lunar Month 15. - 18. Day

17TH

己巳 Earth Snake — *Wood* — ♍
Dipper — Fulfillment — 5 - 1 - 3

★★

00 - 01
01 - 03
03 - 05
05 - 07
07 - 09
09 - 11
11 - 13
13 - 15
15 - 17
17 - 19
19 - 21
21 - 23
23 - 00

50-The Caldron: Sort out material and spiritual ballast and create free space for new ideas.

18FR

庚午 Metal Horse — *Earth* — 07:20 ○ 11:37 ♎
Ox — Balance — 5 - 1 - 4

00 - 01
01 - 03
03 - 05
05 - 07
07 - 09
09 - 11
11 - 13
13 - 15
15 - 17
17 - 19
19 - 21
21 - 23
23 - 00

32-Constancy: Take up a solid position without freezing.

19SA

辛未 Metal Goat — *Earth* — ♎
Maiden — Determination — 5 - 1 - 5

00 - 01
01 - 03
03 - 05
05 - 07
07 - 09
09 - 11
11 - 13
13 - 15
15 - 17
17 - 19
19 - 21
21 - 23
23 - 00

57-Penetrating: Get your goals clear and implement them, gentle but consequent.

20SU

壬申 Water Monkey — *Metal* — 15:46 ♏
Void — Rigidity — 5 - 1 - 6

★★

15:34 Spring Equinox

00 - 01
01 - 03
03 - 05
05 - 07
07 - 09
09 - 11
11 - 13
13 - 15
15 - 17
17 - 19
19 - 21
21 - 23
23 - 00

48-The Well: Develop your potentials and take good care of yourself.

-08:24 EOT 1:00:00 EDT	Year *Metal* Month *Metal*	壬寅 Water Tiger Year 癸卯 Water Rabbit Month 壬寅 Spring Equinox Mar 20 15:34

2022	**WEEK 12**	Water Tiger Year 2. Lunar Month 19. - 21. Day

21 MO

癸酉 Water Rooster — *Metal* — ♏

Roof — Destruction — 5 - 1 - 7

00 - 01
01 - 03
03 - 05
05 - 07
07 - 09
09 - 11
11 - 13
13 - 15
15 - 17
17 - 19
19 - 21
21 - 23
23 - 00

18-Decaying: Do not be too good for humble work. Clear backlog.

22 TU

甲戌 Wood Dog — *Fire* — 18:55 ♐

Room — Danger — 5 - 1 - 8

00 - 01
01 - 03
03 - 05
05 - 07
07 - 09
09 - 11
11 - 13
13 - 15
15 - 17
17 - 19
19 - 21
21 - 23
23 - 00

46-Rising: Rely on your intuition. Put your plans into action - now.

23 WE

乙亥 Wood Pig — *Fire* — ♐

Wall — Completion — 5 - 1 - 9

00 - 01
01 - 03
03 - 05
05 - 07
07 - 09
09 - 11
11 - 13
13 - 15
15 - 17
17 - 19
19 - 21
21 - 23
23 - 00

6-Litigating:
Be honest but not stubborn or impolite. Solve a conflict with empathy and compromising.

-07:14 EOT 1:00:00 EDT	Year *Metal* Month *Metal*	壬寅 Water Tiger Year 癸卯 Water Rabbit Month 壬寅 Spring Equinox

2022	**WEEK 12**	Water Tiger Year 2. Lunar Month 22. - 25. Day

24TH

丙子 Fire Rat — *Water* — 21:55 ♑
Astride — Harvest — 5 - 1 - 1

✹✹ € ✈

€ ✹	00 - 01
♥	01 - 03
✈	03 - 05
∅ ♥ ♥	05 - 07
✹ ♥	07 - 09
✈ ✹	09 - 11
♥ ϟ	11 - 13
∅ ♥ ♥	13 - 15
✹ ♥ ♥	15 - 17
♥ ⏻	17 - 19
	19 - 21
♥ ⏻ ✹	21 - 23
€ ✹	23 - 00

47-Confining: Benefit from your problems for your progress but do not talk about it.

25FR

丁丑 Fire Ox — *Water* — 05:39 ☾ — ♑
Rope — Opening — 5 - 1 - 2

✹✹ ♥ ♥ ✈ ✹

♥	00 - 01
♥ ✹	01 - 03
✈ ✹ ♥	03 - 05
✹ ♥	05 - 07
∅ ♥	07 - 09
♥	09 - 11
♥ €	11 - 13
∅ € ♥ ϟ	13 - 15
✹	15 - 17
♥	17 - 19
∅ ♥	19 - 21
✈ ⏻ ✹	21 - 23
♥ ♥	23 - 00

64-Not Yet Accomplished: Specify precisely what you want to start but finish it definitely.

26SA

戊寅 Earth Tiger — *Earth* — ♑
Stomach — Closing — 5 - 1 - 3

★ ♥ ⏻ ✹

✹ ♥	00 - 01
♥	01 - 03
✹	03 - 05
♥ ✹	05 - 07
€ ♥	07 - 09
∅ ♥ ♥ €	09 - 11
♥	11 - 13
⏻ ✹	13 - 15
∅ ✹ ♥ ✈ ϟ	15 - 17
€ ✹	17 - 19
✹ ♥	19 - 21
✈ ∅ € ✹ ♥	21 - 23
✹ ♥	23 - 00

40-Separating: Disengage yourself from dead weight and return to your roots. Complete necessary objectives immediately.

27SU

己卯 Earth Rabbit — *Earth* — 01:03 ♒
Pleiades — Establishment — 5 - 1 - 4

✹✹ ♥ ⏻ ✈ €
02:00 CET Clock changed to 03:00 CEST

♥ ✹ ♥	00 - 01
∅	01 - 03
✹ ♥	03 - 05
✹	05 - 07
♥ ♥	07 - 09
♥ ✈	09 - 11
♥ €	11 - 13
♥	13 - 15
✈ € ⏻	15 - 17
✹ ♥ ϟ	17 - 19
∅ ♥ ♥	19 - 21
€ ♥	21 - 23
♥ ✹	23 - 00

59-Dispersing: Break deadlocked structures with changes and shared joy.

-06:21 EOT 1:00:00 EDT	Year *Metal* Month *Metal*	壬寅 Water Tiger Year 癸卯 Water Rabbit Month 壬寅 Spring Equinox

2022	WEEK 13	Water Tiger Year 2. Lunar Month 26. - 28. Day

28 MO
庚辰 Metal Dragon — *Metal* — ≈
Net — Removal — 5 - 1 - 5

⚝⚝ ❦ ❥ ✹ ⌀ ✗

♥	00 - 01
₠ ❦ ⏻ ✹	01 - 03
✈	03 - 05
⌀ ❥ ❦	05 - 07
⌀ ❥	07 - 09
✗ ₠	09 - 11
❦	11 - 13
❥	13 - 15
✹ € ♥	15 - 17
✹ ♥ ❦	17 - 19
❦ ϟ	19 - 21
	21 - 23
♥	23 - 00

䷜ 29-Cavern: Be truly and sincere to yourself. Overcome obstacles peacefully.

29 TU
辛巳 Metal Snake — *Metal* — 04:36 ♓
Beak — Fulfillment — 5 - 1 - 6

★★ ♥ € ✈ ❦ ✹

	00 - 01
♥	01 - 03
✗ ₠ ❥ ❦ ✹	03 - 05
₠ ❦	05 - 07
⌀ ✹	07 - 09
⌀	09 - 11
⏻ ✹	11 - 13
✹	13 - 15
⌀ ✹	15 - 17
✹ €	17 - 19
€	19 - 21
✈ ϟ	21 - 23
	23 - 00

䷃ 4-Ignorance: Be enthusiastic and open minded but rely on your experience.

30 WE
壬午 Water Horse — *Wood* — ♓
Orion — Balance — 5 - 1 - 7

⚝ ⌀

❦ € ϟ	00 - 01
⌀ ❥ ❦ ✹	01 - 03
✹ ♥	03 - 05
❦ ⏻	05 - 07
	07 - 09
₠ ⏻ ✹	09 - 11
⌀ ✹ ❥ ❦	11 - 13
⌀ ✹ ♥ ❦	13 - 15
✹ ✈	15 - 17
✹	17 - 19
♥	19 - 21
✗ ❥	21 - 23
❦ € ϟ	23 - 00

䷠ 33-Retiring: A retreat in the right moment saves your dignity. Be insistent.

-05:10 EOT 1:00:00 CEST/EDT	Year *Metal* Month *Metal*	壬寅 Water Tiger Year 癸卯 Water Rabbit Month 壬寅 Spring Equinox

2022	**WEEK 13**	Water Tiger Year 2. Lunar Month 29. Day Water Tiger Year 3. Lunar Month 1. - 3. Day

March

31TH

癸未 Water Goat — *Wood* — 09:26 ♈

Well — Determination — 5 - 1 - 8

★★★ ♥

✹♥♥€	00 - 01
⌀✹♥ϟ	01 - 03
€	03 - 05
⏻✹♥	05 - 07
✹♥	07 - 09
✈⏻	09 - 11
♥♥	11 - 13
€✹	13 - 15
✈€✹	15 - 17
⌀✹♥	17 - 19
⌀♥♥	19 - 21
✹♥	21 - 23
✹♥♥€	23 - 00

31-Influencing:
Reconcile your ambitions and your needs. Use the natural power of attraction of all things.

1FR

甲申 Wood Monkey — *Water* — 06:27 ● ♈

Ghosts — Rigidity — 5 - 1 - 9

★★ϟ ✹⏻ ♥€

♥	00 - 01
⏻✹	01 - 03
⌀♥✈€♥ϟ	03 - 05
♥	05 - 07
€♥	07 - 09
✈⌀€	09 - 11
✹♥	11 - 13
	13 - 15
	15 - 17
€	17 - 19
	19 - 21
⌀♥♥	21 - 23
♥	23 - 00

56-Traveling: Scoop from your inner source, be attentive and start for new shore.

2SA

乙酉 Wood Rooster — *Water* — 16:41 ♉

Willow — Destruction — 5 - 1 - 1

☆☆ϟ ♥♥✹

♥⏻●	00 - 01
⌀♥	01 - 03
✈€	03 - 05
♥€ϟ	05 - 07
⌀♥♥	07 - 09
✹	09 - 11
✹€	11 - 13
✹	13 - 15
⏻●	15 - 17
⌀♥	17 - 19
♥	19 - 21
€✈	21 - 23
♥⏻●	23 - 00

62-Small Testing: Concentrate on the details and complete them with accuracy.

3SU

丙戌 Fire Dog — *Earth* — ♉

Star — Danger — 5 - 1 - 2

☆☆ ♥ ♥✹⌀✈

♥●	00 - 01
⌀€♥	01 - 03
♥	03 - 05
⌀♥♥	05 - 07
✹ϟ	07 - 09
✹€	09 - 11
✹♥	11 - 13
⌀✹♥♥	13 - 15
✈€♥	15 - 17
♥♥⏻●	17 - 19
●	19 - 21
✈€⏻●	21 - 23
♥●	23 - 00

53-Gradually Progressing: Achieve your plans, patient and with integrity.

-04:16 EOT 1:00:00 CEST/EDT	Year *Metal* Month *Metal*	壬寅 Water Tiger Year 癸卯 Water Rabbit Month 壬寅 Spring Equinox

April

2022	WEEK 14	Water Tiger Year · 3. Lunar Month · 4. - 6. Day

4 MO

丁亥 Fire Pig — *Earth* — ♉
Bow — Completion / Danger — 5 - 1/9 - 3

★★ ♥ ⏻ until 19:21
★ ✸ ✗ from 19:21
19:21 Pure Brightness

	00 - 01
	01 - 03
✸♥	03 - 05
€✸♥	05 - 07
	07 - 09
Ø✈⚡	09 - 11
✸€❥	11 - 13
✸♥	13 - 15
✗€♥❥	15 - 17
♥❥⏻✸	17 - 19
Ø€	19 - 21
♥✸	21 - 23
❥	23 - 00

39-Obstructing: Do not bash your head against a wall. Retreat, bethink and talk to friends.

5 TU

戊子 Earth Rat — *Fire* — 02:55 ♊
Wings — Completion — 5 - 9 - 4

★★★ ♥ ✸ € ⏻ ✈

€	00 - 01
⏻♥❥	01 - 03
✈	03 - 05
Ø♥✸	05 - 07
♥❥	07 - 09
✗	09 - 11
✸❥⚡	11 - 13
♥❥	13 - 15
♥	15 - 17
❥	17 - 19
✸	19 - 21
✸♥❥	21 - 23
€	23 - 00

52-Stopping: Make peace with your core and do not get disturbed by emotions.

6 WE

己丑 Earth Ox — *Fire* — ♊
Carriage — Harvest — 5 - 9 - 5

★ ♥ € ✗

⏻✸♥❥	00 - 01
♥✸	01 - 03
✗✸❥	03 - 05
❥	05 - 07
Ø❥	07 - 09
♥	09 - 11
✸♥❥€	11 - 13
Ø€✸♥⚡	13 - 15
⏻	15 - 17
Ø✸♥	17 - 19
Ø♥❥	19 - 21
✈	21 - 23
⏻✸♥	23 - 00

15-Modesty: Be modest but not humble or self-deprecating. Engage in common cause.

-03:06 EOT	Year *Metal*	壬寅 Water Tiger Year 癸卯 Water Rabbit Month	
1:00:00 CEST/EDT	Month *Metal*	壬寅 Water Tiger Year 壬寅 Wood Dragon Month	Apr 04 19:21

2022	**WEEK 14**	Water Tiger Year 3. Lunar Month 7. - 10. Day

April

7TH

庚寅 Metal Tiger *Wood* 15:25 ♋

Horn Opening 5 - 9 - 6

★★ ♥♥ € ⏻ ✈ ✸

♥	00 - 01
✸	01 - 03
✸	03 - 05
♥	05 - 07
€	07 - 09
∅♥♥	09 - 11
♥	11 - 13
⏻	13 - 15
∅✸♥✈€ϟ	15 - 17
€♥	17 - 19
♥♥	19 - 21
✈∅€♥♥	21 - 23
♥	23 - 00

12-Adversity: Keep your balance and listen to your heart. Savor everyday commodities.

8FR

辛卯 Metal Rabbit *Wood* ♋

Neck Closing 5 - 9 - 7

☆ ⏻ ♥♥✸

∅♥	00 - 01
∅	01 - 03
⏻✸	03 - 05
✸	05 - 07
✸♥♥	07 - 09
♥✈	09 - 11
♥⏻€	11 - 13
✸♥	13 - 15
✈€♥	15 - 17
♥€ϟ	17 - 19
∅♥	19 - 21
€♥	21 - 23
∅♥	23 - 00

45-Gathering: Personal sacrifices foster your personal up growth.

9SA

壬辰 Water Dragon *Water* 06:48 ☽ ♋

Base Establishment 5 - 9 - 8

☆ ✈ €

♥	00 - 01
€♥✸	01 - 03
✸✈	03 - 05
♥♥	05 - 07
∅♥	07 - 09
✈€⏻✸	09 - 11
✸	11 - 13
∅♥♥	13 - 15
€♥	15 - 17
♥	17 - 19
ϟ	19 - 21
€	21 - 23
♥	23 - 00

35-Promoting: Be upright, noble and generous. The lust for life evolves from good deeds.

10SU

癸巳 Water Snake *Water* 04:02 ♌

House Removal 5 - 9 - 9

☆☆ ♥✸€∅✈

✸€	00 - 01
✸♥	01 - 03
✈∅€♥♥	03 - 05
€♥⏻✸	05 - 07
∅✸♥	07 - 09
	09 - 11
✸♥	11 - 13
✸	13 - 15
∅♥	15 - 17
	17 - 19
€	19 - 21
✸✈ϟ	21 - 23
✸€	23 - 00

16-Satisfying: Pass your enthusiasm to others. Together you will succeed faster.

-02:16 EOT 1:00:00 CEST/EDT	Year *Metal* Month *Fire*	壬寅 Water Tiger Year 甲辰 Wood Dragon Month 壬寅 Pure Brightness

April

2022	WEEK 15	Water Tiger Year 3. Lunar Month 11. - 13. Day

11 MO

甲午 Wood Horse *Metal* ♌

Heart Fulfillment 5 - 9 - 1

✰̸ ♥ € ✈ ♥♥

♥♥ € ϟ	00 - 01
♥ ♥♥ ✸	01 - 03
€ ♥ ♥♥	03 - 05
♥♥	05 - 07
✸	07 - 09
€̸ ✸ ♥♥	09 - 11
⌀ ✸ ♥	11 - 13
✸ ♥	13 - 15
✸ ✈	15 - 17
	17 - 19
♥	19 - 21
✈̸ €̸ ♥	21 - 23
♥♥ € ϟ	23 - 00

20-Observing: Take the time to take personal stock as a basis for your spiritual growth.

12 TU

乙未 Wood Goat *Metal* 14:19 ♍

Tail Balance 5 - 9 - 2

✰̸✰̸ ♥♥ ⌀

♥ ♥♥ ⏻ ✸	00 - 01
⌀ ♥ ϟ	01 - 03
€	03 - 05
€ ♥	05 - 07
✸ ♥♥	07 - 09
✸ ✈	09 - 11
✸ ♥	11 - 13
€̸	13 - 15
✈̸ €̸ ⏻ ✸	15 - 17
⌀ ♥♥	17 - 19
⌀ ♥	19 - 21
♥	21 - 23
♥ ♥♥ ⏻ ✸	23 - 00

8-Alliance: Do not hesitate to act jointly.

13 WE

丙申 Fire Monkey *Fire* ♍

Basket Determination 5 - 9 - 3

★★ ϟ ♥♥ ✈ €̸

✸ ♥	00 - 01
	01 - 03
⌀ ♥ ✈ ϟ	03 - 05
♥ ♥♥	05 - 07
✸ € ♥	07 - 09
✈̸ ⌀ ✸ ♥♥	09 - 11
♥♥	11 - 13
⌀	13 - 15
✸ ♥♥	15 - 17
€̸ ⏻ ✸	17 - 19
	19 - 21
♥ ♥♥ ✸	21 - 23
✸ ♥	23 - 00

23-Stripping: Dark clouds are rising. Retreat and bethink yourself.

-01:11 EOT 1:00:00 CEST/EDT	Year *Metal* Month *Fire*	壬寅 Water Tiger Year 甲辰 Wood Dragon Month 壬寅 Pure Brightness

2022	**WEEK 15**	Water Tiger Year 3. Lunar Month 14. - 17. Day

April

14TH

丁酉 Fire Rooster — *Fire* — 20:59 ♎
Dipper — Rigidity — 5 - 9 - 4

★ ♥ ✗

♥	00 - 01
∅♥	01 - 03
✗€✸♥	03 - 05
✸♥⚡	05 - 07
∅✸♥	07 - 09
✸	09 - 11
€♥	11 - 13
	13 - 15
	15 - 17
♥✸	17 - 19
♥♥	19 - 21
€✈⏻✸	21 - 23
	23 - 00

䷗ 24-Returning: Something re-enters your life. Clarify your ambitions to get a good start.

15FR

戊戌 Earth Dog — *Wood* — ♎
Ox — Destruction — 5 - 9 - 5

☆☆⚡ ♥✸€
Good Friday

✸♥	00 - 01
€♥♥	01 - 03
♥	03 - 05
∅✸♥	05 - 07
✸♥⚡	07 - 09
✸€	09 - 11
♥	11 - 13
♥♥✸	13 - 15
✈€	15 - 17
♥♥	17 - 19
	19 - 21
✗€✸♥	21 - 23
✸♥	23 - 00

䷚ 27-Jaws: Take care of your corporal and mental nourishment.

16SA

己亥 Earth Pig — *Wood* — 18:57 ○ — ♎
Maiden — Danger — 5 - 9 - 6

★★★ ✸✗

⏻✸♥	00 - 01
	01 - 03
✸♥	03 - 05
€♥	05 - 07
✸	07 - 09
∅✸✈⚡	09 - 11
€	11 - 13
♥	13 - 15
✗€♥♥⏻	15 - 17
✸♥♥	17 - 19
∅€♥	19 - 21
∅♥	21 - 23
⏻✸	23 - 00

䷂ 3-Accumulating: The start is difficult. Be patient and accept help. You will be successful.

17SU

庚子 Metal Rat — *Earth* — 00:28 ♏
Void — Completion — 5 - 9 - 7

★★★ ♥€⏻✈
Easter Sunday

€✸	00 - 01
⏻✸♥	01 - 03
✈	03 - 05
∅♥	05 - 07
✸♥	07 - 09
✗€✸	09 - 11
♥⚡	11 - 13
♥♥	13 - 15
✸€♥	15 - 17
	17 - 19
♥	19 - 21
♥	21 - 23
€✸	23 - 00

䷩ 42-Increasing: Use your abilities for common welfare. Learn from mistakes.

-00:26 EOT 1:00:00 CEST/EDT	Year *Metal* Month *Fire*	壬寅 Water Tiger Year 甲辰 Wood Dragon Month 壬寅 Pure Brightness

2022	WEEK 16	Water Tiger Year 3. Lunar Month 18. - 20. Day

18 MO

辛丑 Metal Ox — *Earth* — ♏
Roof — Harvest — 5 - 9 - 8

★ ♥ € ✈

Easter Monday

♥	00 - 01
♥✸	01 - 03
✈⏻✸	03 - 05
♥	05 - 07
∅✸♥	07 - 09
♥	09 - 11
♥♥⏻✸	11 - 13
∅€✸♥ϟ	13 - 15
♥	15 - 17
∅€♥	17 - 19
∅♥	19 - 21
✈	21 - 23
♥	23 - 00

☳ 51-Startling:
A change is imminent. Keep your calmness and humor, everything will turn to good account.

19 TU

壬寅 Water Tiger — *Metal* — 02:13 ♐
Room — Opening — 5 - 9 - 9

★★★ ♥♥€⏻✈

♥	00 - 01
∅✸	01 - 03
	03 - 05
♥⏻	05 - 07
✸€	07 - 09
♥♥	09 - 11
✸♥♥	11 - 13
✸♥	13 - 15
∅♥✈ϟ	15 - 17
€	17 - 19
♥	19 - 21
✈∅♥♥	21 - 23
♥	23 - 00

䷔ 21-Gnawing And Chewing: Conquer difficulties with discipline and justice.

20 WE

癸卯 Water Rabbit — *Metal* — ♐
Wall — Closing — 5 - 9 - 1

✈ ⏻ ♥♥✸

02:25 Grain Rain

∅✸♥€	00 - 01
∅✸	01 - 03
	03 - 05
⏻✸	05 - 07
♥	07 - 09
♥✈⏻	09 - 11
€	11 - 13
♥	13 - 15
✈€	15 - 17
♥ϟ	17 - 19
∅♥	19 - 21
€✸♥	21 - 23
∅✸♥€	23 - 00

䷐ 17-Following: Learn everything from the scratch and accept advice. This is the basis of authority and recognition.

00:30 EOT 1:00:00 CEST/EDT	Year *Metal* Month *Fire*	壬寅 Water Tiger Year 甲辰 Wood Dragon Month 壬寅 Grain Rain Apr 20 02:25

2022	WEEK **16**	Water Tiger Year 3. Lunar Month 21. - 24. Day

♥	00 - 01
€̸💕̸⏻✹	01 - 03
✹̸✈€💕	03 - 05
⏻̸✹̸♥̸💕̸	05 - 07
⏻̸♥̸	07 - 09
✈̸€̸💕	09 - 11
✹̸💕̸	11 - 13
♥̸✹	13 - 15
✹̸€♥	15 - 17
♥	17 - 19
ϟ	19 - 21
	21 - 23
♥	23 - 00

21 TH

甲辰 Wood Dragon *Fire* 03:48 ♑

Astride Establishment 5 - 9 - 2

☆̸☆̸ ✈ ✹̸ €̸

䷘ 25-Without Wrongdoing: Follow your intuition without calculating intention.

⏻✹	00 - 01
♥	01 - 03
✈̸⏻̸€̸✹̸♥̸💕̸	03 - 05
✹̸💕̸	05 - 07
⏻̸💕	07 - 09
⏻̸	09 - 11
✹̸	11 - 13
✹̸	13 - 15
💕̸✹	15 - 17
	17 - 19
€💕	19 - 21
✈ϟ	21 - 23
⏻✹	23 - 00

22 FR

乙巳 Wood Snake *Fire* ♑

Rope Removal 5 - 9 - 3

☆̸☆̸ 💕̸ ✹̸ €̸ ⏻̸ ✈̸

䷣ 36-Brightness Wounded: Hide your light under a bushel and persecute your aim.

💕̸€✹ϟ	00 - 01
⏻̸♥̸💕̸	01 - 03
✹̸♥	03 - 05
✹̸	05 - 07
✹̸	07 - 09
✹̸	09 - 11
⏻̸♥̸	11 - 13
⏻̸♥	13 - 15
✈💕	15 - 17
⏻✹	17 - 19
♥	19 - 21
✈̸€̸♥̸⏻✹	21 - 23
💕̸€✹ϟ	23 - 00

23 SA

丙午 Fire Horse *Water* 11:58 ☾ 06:21 ♒

Stomach Fulfillment 5 - 9 - 4

☆̸ ♥ € ✈ 💕̸

䷕ 22-Adorning: Design everything functional and beautiful because beauty fosters function.

♥̸💕̸	00 - 01
⏻̸♥̸ϟ	01 - 03
✹̸€💕	03 - 05
✹̸♥	05 - 07
	07 - 09
✈	09 - 11
€♥💕	11 - 13
€̸✹	13 - 15
✈̸€̸	15 - 17
💕̸✹	17 - 19
⏻̸♥̸💕̸	19 - 21
⏻✹♥	21 - 23
♥̸	23 - 00

24 SU

丁未 Fire Goat *Water* ♒

Pleiades Balance 5 - 9 - 5

☆̸☆̸ 💕 ⏻̸

䷾ 63-Already Accomplished: An end is achieved. Finish accurately and prepare for the next begin.

01:08 EOT 1:00:00 CEST/EDT	Year *Metal* Month *Fire*	壬寅 Water Tiger Year 甲辰 Wood Dragon Month 壬寅 Grain Rain

April

2022	**WEEK 17**	Water Tiger Year — 3. Lunar Month — 25. - 27. Day

25 MO

戊申 Earth Monkey — *Earth* — 10:25 ♓

Net — Determination — 5 - 9 - 6

00 - 01	
01 - 03	
03 - 05	
05 - 07	
07 - 09	
09 - 11	
11 - 13	
13 - 15	
15 - 17	
17 - 19	
19 - 21	
21 - 23	
23 - 00	

37-Family: Be reliable and consolidate the output as a solid platform for further developments.

26 TU

己酉 Earth Rooster — *Earth* — ♓

Beak — Rigidity — 5 - 9 - 7

00 - 01	
01 - 03	
03 - 05	
05 - 07	
07 - 09	
09 - 11	
11 - 13	
13 - 15	
15 - 17	
17 - 19	
19 - 21	
21 - 23	
23 - 00	

55-Overshadowing: Use your wealth with wisdom for your ambitions.

27 WE

庚戌 Metal Dog — *Metal* — 16:17 ♈

Orion — Destruction — 5 - 9 - 8

00 - 01	
01 - 03	
03 - 05	
05 - 07	
07 - 09	
09 - 11	
11 - 13	
13 - 15	
15 - 17	
17 - 19	
19 - 21	
21 - 23	
23 - 00	

30-Brightness: Light your inner fire. Enlighten dark corners and unsettled affairs.

01:53 EOT 1:00:00 CEST/EDT	Year *Metal* Month *Fire*	壬寅 Water Tiger Year 甲辰 Wood Dragon Month 壬寅 Grain Rain

2022	**WEEK 17**	Water Tiger Year 3. Lunar Month 28. - 30. Day Water Tiger Year 4. Lunar Month 1. Day

28TH

辛亥 Metal Pig — *Metal* — ♈
Well — Danger — 5 - 9 - 9

☆̸ 💕 ✸ ✈̸

	00 - 01
	01 - 03
💕 ⏻ ♥	03 - 05
₠ ✸ ♥	05 - 07
✸	07 - 09
∅ ✈ ⚡	09 - 11
⏻ ✹	11 - 13
✸ ♥	13 - 15
✈̸ ₠ ❥	15 - 17
❥ 💕 €	17 - 19
∅ €	19 - 21
∅ ❥	21 - 23
	23 - 00

䷰ 49-Reforming: It is a convenient time for changes. Trust in your competence be persistent.

29FR

壬子 Water Rat — *Wood* — ♈
Ghosts — Completion — 5 - 9 - 1

★ ♥ ✹ € ⏻ ✈

€ ✹	00 - 01
✹ ♥	01 - 03
✸ ✈	03 - 05
❥	05 - 07
♥	07 - 09
✈̸ ₠ ⏻ ✹	09 - 11
✸ ⚡	11 - 13
∅ ❥ ✹	13 - 15
♥	15 - 17
💕	17 - 19
	19 - 21
❥ €	21 - 23
€ ✹	23 - 00

䷒ 19-Arriving: Seize the opportunity. Invest in your future.

30SA

癸丑 Water Ox — *Wood* — 20:30 ● 00:18 ♉
Willow — Harvest — 5 - 9 - 2

☆̸ ♥ € ✈̸

✸ € ♥	00 - 01
❥	01 - 03
✈̸ ✸	03 - 05
💕 ⏻	05 - 07
∅ ✹	07 - 09
⏻ ♥	09 - 11
❥	11 - 13
∅ ₠ ❥ ⚡	13 - 15
	15 - 17
∅ ♥	17 - 19
∅ ❥	19 - 21
✸ ✈	21 - 23
✸ € ♥	23 - 00

䷨ 41-Decreasing: Affiliate honesty with self-restraint. Small things provoke big ones.

1SU

甲寅 Wood Tiger — *Water* — ♉
Star — Opening — 5 - 9 - 3

★★ 💕 ♥ € ✈ ✸
Labour Day

✸ 💕	00 - 01
	01 - 03
€ ✹ 💕	03 - 05
❥	05 - 07
€	07 - 09
∅ ❥	09 - 11
✸ ♥	11 - 13
⏻ ✹	13 - 15
∅ ✸ ❥ ✈ ⚡	15 - 17
₠	17 - 19
♥	19 - 21
✈̸ ∅ ₠ 💕 ♥	21 - 23
✸ 💕	23 - 00

䷻ 60-Regulating: Identify your limitations. Extend suffocating ones, establish wise ones.

02:21 EOT 1:00:00 CEST/EDT	Year *Metal* Month *Fire*	壬寅 Water Tiger Year 甲辰 Wood Dragon Month 壬寅 Grain Rain

April

2022	WEEK 18	Water Tiger Year 4. Lunar Month 2. - 4. Day

2 MO

乙卯 Wood Rabbit — *Water* — 10:40 ♊
Bow — Closing — 5 - 9 - 4

✈̸ ⏻ ♥♥ ♥ ✸

♥	00 - 01
∅✸	01 - 03
	03 - 05
€✸	05 - 07
♥	07 - 09
✸♥✈	09 - 11
✸♥♥€	11 - 13
✸♥	13 - 15
✈̸€̸⏻✸	15 - 17
♥♥⚡	17 - 19
∅♥♥♥	19 - 21
€̸♥	21 - 23
♥	23 - 00

☴☱ 61-Mutually Trusting: Have an open mind and search for the true core. This arises understanding, adjacency and continuance.

3 TU

丙辰 Fire Dragon — *Earth* — ♊
Wings — Establishment — 5 - 9 - 5

✈̸ ✈ ✸ €̸

♥	00 - 01
€̸✸♥♥	01 - 03
✈	03 - 05
∅♥	05 - 07
∅✸♥	07 - 09
✈̸✸	09 - 11
♥♥	11 - 13
∅♥	13 - 15
€♥♥♥	15 - 17
⏻✸♥	17 - 19
⚡	19 - 21
⏻✸	21 - 23
♥	23 - 00

☳☱ 54-The Libidinal Addiction: Be true to your emotions and addiction but with retention.

4 WE

丁巳 Fire Snake — *Earth* — 22:53 ♋
Carriage — Removal — 5 - 9 - 6

★★★ ⚡ ✸ €̸ ∅ ✈̸

✸	00 - 01
✸♥	01 - 03
✈̸∅€̸✸♥	03 - 05
€̸✸♥♥	05 - 07
∅	07 - 09
∅✸	09 - 11
€♥♥	11 - 13
	13 - 15
∅♥♥	15 - 17
⏻✸	17 - 19
€	19 - 21
✈⏻✸⚡	21 - 23
✸♥♥	23 - 00

☲☱ 38-Misunderstanding:
Remain true to yourself. Develop individual differences to constructive connections.

02:52 EOT 1:00:00 CEST/EDT	Year *Metal* Month *Fire*	壬寅 Water Tiger Year 甲辰 Wood Dragon Month 壬寅 Grain Rain

2022	WEEK 18	Water Tiger Year 4. Lunar Month 5. - 8. Day

May

5TH

戊午 Earth Horse — *Fire* — ♋

Horn — Fulfillment / Removal — 5 - 9/8 - 7

☆ ♥ € ✈ ♥ — until 12:27

☆ ♥ Ø ✶ — from 12:27

12:27 Coming of Summer

✸♥€ϟ	00 - 01
♥	01 - 03
♥	03 - 05
♥✸	05 - 07
♥	07 - 09
	09 - 11
Ø♥	11 - 13
✸♥	13 - 15
✈	15 - 17
	17 - 19
✸♥	19 - 21
✶€✸♥♥	21 - 23
✸♥€ϟ	23 - 00

☱ 58-Pleasing: With an inner smile about yourself and the world you will win the hearts of other people and free your own.

6FR

己未 Earth Goat — *Fire* — ♋

Neck — Fulfillment — 5 - 8 - 8

★★ ♥ € ⏻ ✈

♥⏻	00 - 01
Ø✸♥ϟ	01 - 03
€✸♥	03 - 05
♥	05 - 07
	07 - 09
✈	09 - 11
€♥	11 - 13
€✸	13 - 15
✶€⏻	15 - 17
Ø✸♥	17 - 19
Ø♥	19 - 21
♥	21 - 23
♥♥⏻	23 - 00

☰ 10-Treading: Show self-confidence and inner strength together with sereneness.

7SA

庚申 Metal Monkey — *Wood* — 11:38 ♌

Base — Balance — 5 - 8 - 9

★ ϟ ✸ ✈

✸♥	00 - 01
⏻	01 - 03
Ø♥✈ϟ	03 - 05
♥	05 - 07
€♥	07 - 09
✶Ø€♥	09 - 11
♥	11 - 13
	13 - 15
€	15 - 17
€♥	17 - 19
♥	19 - 21
Ø♥♥	21 - 23
✸♥	23 - 00

☷ 11-Prominence: Work together and complement one another. Everyone will profit.

8SU

辛酉 Metal Rooster — *Wood* — ♌

House — Determination — 5 - 8 - 1

☆ ♥ ⏻

✸♥	00 - 01
Ø✸♥	01 - 03
✶€⏻✸	03 - 05
♥ϟ	05 - 07
Ø✸♥	07 - 09
	09 - 11
⏻€✸	11 - 13
✸	13 - 15
♥	15 - 17
Ø♥€	17 - 19
♥♥	19 - 21
€✈	21 - 23
✸♥	23 - 00

☶ 26-Great Gains: Focus your strength. Go out and utilize your capabilities profitably.

03:09 EOT 1:00:00 CEST/EDT	Year *Metal* Month *Fire*	壬寅 Water Tiger Year 甲辰 Wood Dragon Month 壬寅 Water Tiger Year 壬寅 Wood Snake Month — May 05 12:27

2022	WEEK 19	Water Tiger Year	4. Lunar Month	9. - 11. Day

9 MO

壬戌 Water Dog — *Water* — 00:22 ☽ 22:52 ♍

Heart — Rigidity — 5 - 8 - 2

00 - 01
01 - 03
03 - 05
05 - 07
07 - 09
09 - 11
11 - 13
13 - 15
15 - 17
17 - 19
19 - 21
21 - 23
23 - 00

5-Waiting: Be patient and pursue your goal, step by step.

10 TU

癸亥 Water Pig — *Water* — ♍

Tail — Destruction — 5 - 8 - 3

00 - 01
01 - 03
03 - 05
05 - 07
07 - 09
09 - 11
11 - 13
13 - 15
15 - 17
17 - 19
19 - 21
21 - 23
23 - 00

9-Small Savings: Go for your ambition with small steps instead of great leaps.

11 WE

甲子 Wood Rat — *Metal* — ♍

Basket — Danger — 5 - 8 - 4

00 - 01
01 - 03
03 - 05
05 - 07
07 - 09
09 - 11
11 - 13
13 - 15
15 - 17
17 - 19
19 - 21
21 - 23
23 - 00

34-Great Strength: Check your handling of power. Grandeur and justice belong together.

03:25 EOT 1:00:00 CEST/EDT	Year *Metal* Month *Fire*	壬寅 Water Tiger Year 乙巳 Wood Snake Month 壬寅 Coming of Summer

2022	**WEEK 19**	Water Tiger Year · 4. Lunar Month · 12. - 15. Day

May

12TH

乙丑 Wood Ox — *Metal* — 06:42 ♎

Dipper — Completion — 5 - 8 - 5

★ ♥♥ ♥ ✸ € ✈

⏻✸♥	00 - 01
♥✸	01 - 03
✸	03 - 05
♥€	05 - 07
∅	07 - 09
✸♥	09 - 11
✸♥♥	11 - 13
∅€✸♥⚡	13 - 15
⏻✸	15 - 17
∅♥	17 - 19
∅✸♥♥	19 - 21
✸✈	21 - 23
⏻✸♥	23 - 00

14-Great Reward: Use your capabilities and assets for common weal.

13FR

丙寅 Fire Tiger — *Fire* — ♎

Ox — Harvest — 5 - 8 - 6

∅ ✸✸

♥✸	00 - 01
∅	01 - 03
✸	03 - 05
♥♥	05 - 07
✸€	07 - 09
∅✸♥♥€	09 - 11
♥	11 - 13
	13 - 15
∅♥✈♥⚡	15 - 17
€⏻✸	17 - 19
✸♥	19 - 21
✸€♥♥	21 - 23
♥✸	23 - 00

43-Severing: Stand up frankly for your own truth. Be determined but not offending.

14SA

丁卯 Fire Rabbit — *Fire* — 10:41 ♏

Maiden — Opening — 5 - 8 - 7

★ ♥ € ✈ ✸

∅♥	00 - 01
∅	01 - 03
✸♥	03 - 05
	05 - 07
♥♥	07 - 09
♥✈	09 - 11
€	11 - 13
♥	13 - 15
✸€	15 - 17
♥⏻✸⚡	17 - 19
∅✸♥	19 - 21
€⏻♥	21 - 23
∅♥♥	23 - 00

44-Meeting: Examine a seductive offer with minuteness and hold off.

15SU

戊辰 Earth Dragon — *Wood* — ♏

Void — Closing — 5 - 8 - 8

∅∅ ✸

✸♥	00 - 01
€⏻	01 - 03
✈	03 - 05
∅♥♥✸	05 - 07
∅♥♥	07 - 09
✸	09 - 11
♥	11 - 13
♥✸	13 - 15
€♥	15 - 17
♥	17 - 19
✸⚡	19 - 21
✸♥	21 - 23
✸♥	23 - 00

28-Great Test: Do not blow your plans out of proportions. Be gentle and mind your balance.

03:31 EOT 1:00:00 CEST/EDT	Year *Metal* Month *Fire*	壬寅 Water Tiger Year 乙巳 Wood Snake Month 壬寅 Coming of Summer

May

2022	**WEEK 20**	Water Tiger Year 4. Lunar Month 16. - 18. Day

16 MO

己巳 Earth Snake *Wood* 04:15 ○ 11:49 ♐
Roof Establishment 5 - 8 - 9

☆☆ ♥ ⏻ ✈ ♥ ✸ €

⏻ ✸ ♥	00 - 01
♥	01 - 03
✈ Ø € ♥ ✸	03 - 05
€ ♥	05 - 07
Ø	07 - 09
Ø ✸	09 - 11
€	11 - 13
	13 - 15
♥	15 - 17
✸	17 - 19
✸ € ♥	19 - 21
✸ ✈ ϟ	21 - 23
⏻ ✸	23 - 00

䷱ 50-The Caldron: Sort out material and spiritual ballast and create free space for new ideas.

17 TU

庚午 Metal Horse *Earth* ♐
Room Removal 5 - 8 - 1

★★★ ✸ ✈

♥ € ϟ	00 - 01
♥ ♥ ✸	01 - 03
♥	03 - 05
♥	05 - 07
	07 - 09
€	09 - 11
Ø ♥	11 - 13
♥	13 - 15
✸ ✈ €	15 - 17
♥	17 - 19
✸ ♥ ♥	19 - 21
✈ € ✸ ♥	21 - 23
♥ € ϟ	23 - 00

䷟ 32-Constancy: Take up a solid position without freezing.

18 WE

辛未 Metal Goat *Earth* 11:54 ♑
Wall Fulfillment 5 - 8 - 2

★★ ♥ € ⏻ ✈

♥ ♥	00 - 01
Ø ♥ ϟ	01 - 03
⏻ € ✸	03 - 05
♥	05 - 07
✸	07 - 09
✈	09 - 11
⏻ ✸ ♥	11 - 13
€	13 - 15
✈ € ♥	15 - 17
Ø ♥ €	17 - 19
Ø ✸ ♥ ♥	19 - 21
✸ ♥	21 - 23
♥ ♥	23 - 00

䷸ 57-Penetrating: Get your goals clear and implement them, gentle but consequent.

03:31 EOT 1:00:00 CEST/EDT	Year *Metal* Month *Fire*	壬寅 Water Tiger Year 乙巳 Wood Snake Month 壬寅 Coming of Summer

2022	WEEK 20	Water Tiger Year 4. Lunar Month 19. - 22. Day

May

19TH

壬申 Water Monkey — *Metal* — ♑

Astride — Balance — 5 - 8 - 3

00 - 01
01 - 03
03 - 05
05 - 07
07 - 09
09 - 11
11 - 13
13 - 15
15 - 17
17 - 19
19 - 21
21 - 23
23 - 00

48-The Well: Develop your potentials and take good care of yourself.

20FR

癸酉 Water Rooster — *Metal* — 12:48 ♒

Rope — Determination — 5 - 8 - 4

00 - 01
01 - 03
03 - 05
05 - 07
07 - 09
09 - 11
11 - 13
13 - 15
15 - 17
17 - 19
19 - 21
21 - 23
23 - 00

18-Decaying: Do not be too good for humble work. Clear backlog.

21SA

甲戌 Wood Dog — *Fire* — ♒

Stomach — Rigidity — 5 - 8 - 5

01:23 Small Sprout

00 - 01
01 - 03
03 - 05
05 - 07
07 - 09
09 - 11
11 - 13
13 - 15
15 - 17
17 - 19
19 - 21
21 - 23
23 - 00

46-Rising: Rely on your intuition. Put your plans into action - now.

22SU

乙亥 Wood Pig — *Fire* — 18:44 ☾ 15:54 ♓

Pleiades — Destruction — 5 - 8 - 6

00 - 01
01 - 03
03 - 05
05 - 07
07 - 09
09 - 11
11 - 13
13 - 15
15 - 17
17 - 19
19 - 21
21 - 23
23 - 00

6-Litigating:
Be honest but not stubborn or impolite. Solve a conflict with empathy and compromising.

03:25 EOT 1:00:00 CEST/EDT	Year *Metal* Month *Fire*	壬寅 Water Tiger Year 乙巳 Wood Snake Month 壬寅 Small Sprout May 21 01:23

May

2022	WEEK 21	Water Tiger Year 4. Lunar Month 23. - 25. Day

23 MO

丙子 Fire Rat — *Water* — ♓
Net — Danger — 5 - 8 - 7

★★ ✸

€ ✸	00 - 01
♥	01 - 03
✈	03 - 05
∅ ♥	05 - 07
✸ ♥	07 - 09
✸	09 - 11
ϟ	11 - 13
∅ ♥	13 - 15
✸ ♥	15 - 17
⏻	17 - 19
	19 - 21
♥ ⏻ ✸	21 - 23
€ ✸	23 - 00

䷮ 47-Confining: Benefit from your problems for your progress but do not talk about it.

24 TU

丁丑 Fire Ox — *Water* — 21:50 ♈
Beak — Completion — 5 - 8 - 8

★ ♥ ♥ ✸ € ✈

♥	00 - 01
♥ ✸	01 - 03
✸ ♥	03 - 05
✸ ♥	05 - 07
∅ ♥	07 - 09
♥	09 - 11
♥ €	11 - 13
∅ € ♥ ϟ	13 - 15
✸	15 - 17
♥	17 - 19
∅ ♥	19 - 21
✈ ⏻ ✸	21 - 23
♥ ♥	23 - 00

䷿ 64-Not Yet Accomplished: Specify precisely what you want to start but finish it definitely.

25 WE

戊寅 Earth Tiger — *Earth* — ♈
Orion — Harvest — 5 - 8 - 9

☆☆ ✸

✸ ♥	00 - 01
♥	01 - 03
✸	03 - 05
♥ ✸	05 - 07
€ ♥	07 - 09
∅ ♥ ♥ €	09 - 11
♥	11 - 13
⏻ ✸	13 - 15
∅ ✸ ♥ ✈ ϟ	15 - 17
€ ✸	17 - 19
✸ ♥	19 - 21
∅ € ✸ ♥	21 - 23
✸ ♥	23 - 00

䷧ 40-Separating: Disengage yourself from dead weight and return to your roots. Complete necessary objectives immediately.

03:09 EOT 1:00:00 CEST/EDT	Year *Metal* Month *Fire*	壬寅 Water Tiger Year 乙巳 Wood Snake Month 壬寅 Small Sprout

2022	**WEEK 21**	Water Tiger Year 4. Lunar Month 26. - 29. Day

May

26TH

己卯 Earth Rabbit — *Earth* — ♈
Well — Opening — 5 - 8 - 1
★★★ ♥ € ⏻ ✈ ✹
Ascension

♥✹♥	00 - 01
⌀	01 - 03
✹♥	03 - 05
✹	05 - 07
♥♥	07 - 09
♥✈	09 - 11
♥€	11 - 13
♥	13 - 15
✳€⏻	15 - 17
✹♥ϟ	17 - 19
⌀♥♥	19 - 21
€♥	21 - 23
♥✹	23 - 00

59-Dispersing: Break deadlocked structures with changes and shared joy.

27FR

庚辰 Metal Dragon — *Metal* — 06:32 ♉
Ghosts — Closing — 5 - 8 - 2
✳ ♥

♥	00 - 01
€♥⏻✹	01 - 03
✈	03 - 05
⌀♥♥	05 - 07
⌀♥	07 - 09
✳€	09 - 11
♥	11 - 13
♥	13 - 15
✹€♥	15 - 17
✹♥♥	17 - 19
♥ϟ	19 - 21
	21 - 23
♥	23 - 00

29-Cavern: Be truly and sincere to yourself. Overcome obstacles peacefully.

28SA

辛巳 Metal Snake — *Metal* — ♉
Willow — Establishment — 5 - 8 - 3
✳ ♥ ⏻ ✈ ♥ €

	00 - 01
♥	01 - 03
✳€♥♥✹	03 - 05
€♥	05 - 07
⌀✹	07 - 09
⌀	09 - 11
⏻✹	11 - 13
✹	13 - 15
⌀✹	15 - 17
✹€	17 - 19
€	19 - 21
✈ϟ	21 - 23
	23 - 00

4-Ignorance: Be enthusiastic and open minded but rely on your experience.

29SU

壬午 Water Horse — *Wood* — 17:25 ♊
Star — Removal — 5 - 8 - 4
★★★ ♥ ⌀ ✳

♥€ϟ	00 - 01
⌀♥♥✹	01 - 03
✹♥	03 - 05
♥⏻	05 - 07
	07 - 09
€⏻✹	09 - 11
⌀✹♥♥	11 - 13
⌀✹♥♥	13 - 15
✹✈	15 - 17
✹	17 - 19
♥	19 - 21
✳♥	21 - 23
♥€ϟ	23 - 00

33-Retiring: A retreat in the right moment saves your dignity. Be insistent.

02:52 EOT 1:00:00 CEST/EDT	Year *Metal* Month *Fire*	壬寅 Water Tiger Year 乙巳 Wood Snake Month 壬寅 Small Sprout

May

2022	**WEEK 22**	Water Tiger Year · 5. Lunar Month · 1. - 3. Day

30 MO

癸未 Water Goat — *Wood* — 11:32 ● — ♊

Bow — Fulfillment — 5 - 8 - 5

⌀̸ ♥ € ✈

✸♥❦€	00 - 01
⌀✸♥ϟ	01 - 03
€	03 - 05
⏻✸♥	05 - 07
✸❦	07 - 09
✈⏻	09 - 11
♥❦	11 - 13
€̸✸	13 - 15
✈̸€̸✸	15 - 17
⌀✸❦	17 - 19
⌀♥❦	19 - 21
✸♥	21 - 23
✸♥❦€	23 - 00

䷞ 31-Influencing:
Reconcile your ambitions and your needs. Use the natural power of attraction of all things.

31 TU

甲申 Wood Monkey — *Water* — ♊

Wings — Balance — 5 - 8 - 6

⌀̸⌀̸ϟ ✈ ⌀

♥	00 - 01
⏻✸	01 - 03
⌀♥✈€❦ϟ	03 - 05
♥	05 - 07
€♥	07 - 09
✈̸⌀€̸	09 - 11
✸❦	11 - 13
	13 - 15
	15 - 17
€̸	17 - 19
	19 - 21
⌀♥❦	21 - 23
♥	23 - 00

䷷ 56-Traveling: Scoop from your inner source, be attentive and start for new shore.

1 WE

乙酉 Wood Rooster — *Water* — 05:42 ♋

Carriage — Determination — 5 - 8 - 7

⌀̸ ❦

❦⏻✸	00 - 01
⌀♥	01 - 03
✈̸€̸	03 - 05
❦€ϟ	05 - 07
⌀♥❦	07 - 09
✸	09 - 11
✸€	11 - 13
✸	13 - 15
⏻✸	15 - 17
⌀♥	17 - 19
♥	19 - 21
€̸✈	21 - 23
❦⏻✸	23 - 00

䷽ 62-Small Testing: Concentrate on the details and complete them with accuracy.

02:23 EOT 1:00:00 CEST/EDT	Year *Metal* Month *Fire*	壬寅 Water Tiger Year 乙巳 Wood Snake Month 壬寅 Small Sprout

2022	**WEEK 22**	Water Tiger Year 5. Lunar Month 4. - 7. Day

June

2TH

丙戌 Fire Dog — *Earth* — ♋
Horn — Rigidity — 5 - 8 - 8

♥♥✹	00 - 01
ø€♥	01 - 03
♥	03 - 05
ø♥♥	05 - 07
✹ϟ	07 - 09
✹€	09 - 11
✹♥	11 - 13
ø✹♥♥	13 - 15
✈€♥	15 - 17
♥♥⏻✹	17 - 19
✹	19 - 21
✶€⏻✹	21 - 23
♥✹	23 - 00

☆☆ ♥✶

䷴ 53-Gradually Progressing: Achieve your plans, patient and with integrity.

3FR

丁亥 Fire Pig — *Earth* — 18:23 ♌
Neck — Destruction — 5 - 8 - 9

	00 - 01
	01 - 03
✹♥	03 - 05
€✹♥	05 - 07
	07 - 09
ø✈ϟ	09 - 11
✹€♥	11 - 13
✹♥	13 - 15
✶€♥♥	15 - 17
♥♥⏻✹	17 - 19
ø€	19 - 21
♥✹	21 - 23
♥	23 - 00

☆☆ϟ ♥✹

䷦ 39-Obstructing: Do not bash your head against a wall. Retreat, bethink and talk to friends.

4SA

戊子 Earth Rat — *Fire* — ♌
Base — Danger — 5 - 8 - 1

€	00 - 01
⏻♥♥	01 - 03
✈	03 - 05
ø♥✹	05 - 07
♥♥	07 - 09
✶	09 - 11
✹♥ϟ	11 - 13
♥♥	13 - 15
♥	15 - 17
♥	17 - 19
✹	19 - 21
✹♥♥	21 - 23
€	23 - 00

★ ♥✹✶

䷳ 52-Stopping: Make peace with your core and do not get disturbed by emotions.

5SU

己丑 Earth Ox — *Fire* — ♌
House — Completion / Danger — 5 - 8/7 - 2

⏻✹♥♥	00 - 01
♥✹	01 - 03
✶✹♥	03 - 05
♥	05 - 07
ø♥	07 - 09
♥	09 - 11
✹♥♥€	11 - 13
ø€✹♥ϟ	13 - 15
⏻	15 - 17
ø✹♥	17 - 19
ø♥♥	19 - 21
✈	21 - 23
⏻✹♥	23 - 00

★ ♥♥✹€✈ — until 16:26
☆☆ ♥♥✹ø✶ — from 16:26

16:26 Planting of Grain
Whit Sunday

䷎ 15-Modesty: Be modest but not humble or self-deprecating. Engage in common cause.

01:56 EOT 1:00:00 CEST/EDT	Year *Metal* Month *Fire*	壬寅 Water Tiger Year 乙巳 Wood Snake Month 壬寅 Water Tiger Year 壬寅 Fire Horse Month Jun 05 16:26

2022	**WEEK 23**	Water Tiger Year 5. Lunar Month 8. - 10. Day

6 MO

庚寅 Metal Tiger — *Wood* — 06:07 ♍
Heart — Completion — 5 - 7 - 3

★★★ ♥♥ ♥ € ⏻ ✈
Whit Monday

♥♥	00 - 01
✸	01 - 03
✸	03 - 05
♥	05 - 07
€	07 - 09
∅♥♥♥	09 - 11
♥	11 - 13
⏻	13 - 15
∅✸̸♥✈€ϟ	15 - 17
€̸♥♥	17 - 19
♥♥♥	19 - 21
✈̸∅€̸♥♥♥	21 - 23
♥♥	23 - 00

☰☷ 12-Adversity: Keep your balance and listen to your heart. Savor everyday commodities.

7 TU

辛卯 Metal Rabbit — *Wood* — 14:49 ☽ ♍
Tail — Harvest — 5 - 7 - 4

✫̸ ♥ € ⏻ ✸̸ ✈̸

∅♥	00 - 01
∅	01 - 03
⏻✸	03 - 05
✸	05 - 07
✸̸♥♥♥	07 - 09
♥✈	09 - 11
♥♥⏻€	11 - 13
✸̸♥	13 - 15
✈̸€̸♥♥	15 - 17
♥♥€ϟ	17 - 19
∅♥	19 - 21
€̸♥	21 - 23
∅♥	23 - 00

☷☱ 45-Gathering: Personal sacrifices foster your personal up growth.

8 WE

壬辰 Water Dragon — *Water* — 15:19 ♎
Basket — Opening — 5 - 7 - 5

★★★ ♥♥ ♥ ✈ ✸̸

♥	00 - 01
€̸♥♥✸	01 - 03
✸̸✈	03 - 05
♥♥♥	05 - 07
∅♥	07 - 09
✈̸€̸⏻✸	09 - 11
✸̸	11 - 13
∅♥♥♥	13 - 15
€♥	15 - 17
♥	17 - 19
ϟ	19 - 21
€	21 - 23
♥	23 - 00

☲☷ 35-Promoting: Be upright, noble and generous. The lust for life evolves from good deeds.

01:16 EOT 1:00:00 CEST/EDT	Year *Metal* Month *Water*	壬寅 Water Tiger Year 丙午 Fire Horse Month 壬寅 Planting of Grain

2022	**WEEK 23**	Water Tiger Year 5. Lunar Month 11. - 14. Day

June

9TH

癸巳 Water Snake — *Water* — ♎

Dipper — Closing — 5 - 7 - 6

✫✫ € ⏻ ♥ ✸

✸€	00 - 01
✸♥	01 - 03
✶⌀€♥♥	03 - 05
€♥⏻✸	05 - 07
⌀✸♥	07 - 09
	09 - 11
✸♥	11 - 13
✸	13 - 15
⌀♥	15 - 17
	17 - 19
€	19 - 21
✸✈ϟ	21 - 23
✸€	23 - 00

☳☷ 16-Satisfying: Pass your enthusiasm to others. Together you will succeed faster.

10FR

甲午 Wood Horse — *Metal* — 20:44 ♏

Ox — Establishment — 5 - 7 - 7

★ ✈ €

♥€ϟ	00 - 01
♥♥✸	01 - 03
€♥♥	03 - 05
♥	05 - 07
✸	07 - 09
€✸♥	09 - 11
⌀✸♥	11 - 13
✸♥	13 - 15
✸✈	15 - 17
	17 - 19
♥	19 - 21
✶€♥	21 - 23
♥€ϟ	23 - 00

☴☷ 20-Observing: Take the time to take personal stock as a basis for your spiritual growth.

11SA

乙未 Wood Goat — *Metal* — ♏

Maiden — Removal — 5 - 7 - 8

✫✫ ♥ ♥⌀✶

♥♥⏻✸	00 - 01
⌀♥ϟ	01 - 03
€	03 - 05
€♥	05 - 07
✸♥	07 - 09
✸✈	09 - 11
✸♥	11 - 13
€	13 - 15
✶€⏻✸	15 - 17
⌀♥	17 - 19
⌀♥	19 - 21
♥	21 - 23
♥♥⏻✸	23 - 00

☵☷ 8-Alliance: Do not hesitate to act jointly.

12SU

丙申 Fire Monkey — *Fire* — 22:33 ♐

Void — Fulfillment — 5 - 7 - 9

★★ϟ ♥ ✸ ⏻ ✈

✸♥	00 - 01
	01 - 03
⌀♥✈ϟ	03 - 05
♥♥	05 - 07
✸€♥	07 - 09
✶⌀✸♥	09 - 11
♥	11 - 13
⌀	13 - 15
✸♥	15 - 17
€⏻✸	17 - 19
	19 - 21
♥♥✸	21 - 23
✸♥	23 - 00

☶☷ 23-Stripping: Dark clouds are rising. Retreat and bethink yourself.

00:42 EOT 1:00:00 CEST/EDT	Year *Metal* Month *Water*	壬寅 Water Tiger Year 丙午 Fire Horse Month 壬寅 Planting of Grain

June

2022	WEEK 24	Water Tiger Year 5. Lunar Month 15. - 17. Day

13 MO

丁酉 Fire Rooster — *Fire* — ♐
Roof — Balance — 5 - 7 - 1

☆☆ ♥ ø

♥	00 - 01
ø♥	01 - 03
✈€✸♥	03 - 05
✸♥ϟ	05 - 07
ø✸♥	07 - 09
✸	09 - 11
€♥	11 - 13
	13 - 15
	15 - 17
♥✸	17 - 19
♥♥	19 - 21
€✈⏻✸	21 - 23
	23 - 00

☷ 24-Returning: Something re-enters your life. Clarify your ambitions to get a good start.

14 TU

戊戌 Earth Dog — *Wood* — 11:52 ○ 22:09 ♑
Room — Determination — 5 - 7 - 2

★★★ϟ ♥⏻ €

✸♥	00 - 01
€♥♥	01 - 03
♥	03 - 05
ø✸♥	05 - 07
✸♥ϟ	07 - 09
✸€	09 - 11
♥	11 - 13
♥♥✸	13 - 15
✈€	15 - 17
♥♥	17 - 19
	19 - 21
✈€✸♥	21 - 23
✸♥	23 - 00

☶ 27-Jaws: Take care of your corporal and mental nourishment.

15 WE

己亥 Earth Pig — *Wood* — ♑
Wall — Rigidity — 5 - 7 - 3

★★ ✸⏻ ♥✈

⏻✸♥	00 - 01
	01 - 03
✸♥	03 - 05
€♥	05 - 07
✸	07 - 09
ø✸✈ϟ	09 - 11
€	11 - 13
♥	13 - 15
✈€♥♥⏻	15 - 17
✸♥♥	17 - 19
ø€♥	19 - 21
ø♥	21 - 23
⏻✸	23 - 00

☵ 3-Accumulating: The start is difficult. Be patient and accept help. You will be successful.

-00:06 EOT 1:00:00 CEST/EDT	Year *Metal* Month *Water*	壬寅 Water Tiger Year 丙午 Fire Horse Month 壬寅 Planting of Grain

2022	**WEEK 24**	Water Tiger Year 5. Lunar Month 18. - 21. Day

June

16TH

庚子 Metal Rat | *Earth* | 21:35 ♒
Astride | Destruction | 5 - 7 - 4

✫✫ϟ ♥♥✸

€✸	00 - 01
⏻✸♥	01 - 03
✈	03 - 05
ø♥	05 - 07
✸♥	07 - 09
✈€✸	09 - 11
♥ϟ	11 - 13
♥♥	13 - 15
✸€♥	15 - 17
	17 - 19
♥	19 - 21
♥	21 - 23
€✸	23 - 00

☴☳ 42-Increasing: Use your abilities for common welfare. Learn from mistakes.

17FR

辛丑 Metal Ox | *Earth* | ♒
Rope | Danger | 5 - 7 - 5

✫✫ ♥✸ø✈

♥	00 - 01
♥✸	01 - 03
✈⏻✸	03 - 05
♥	05 - 07
ø✸♥	07 - 09
♥	09 - 11
♥♥⏻✸	11 - 13
ø€✸♥ϟ	13 - 15
♥	15 - 17
ø€♥	17 - 19
ø♥	19 - 21
✈	21 - 23
♥	23 - 00

☳☳ 51-Startling:
A change is imminent. Keep your calmness and humor, everything will turn to good account.

18SA

壬寅 Water Tiger | *Metal* | 22:56 ♓
Stomach | Completion | 5 - 7 - 6

★★ ♥♥€⏻✈

♥	00 - 01
ø✸	01 - 03
	03 - 05
♥⏻	05 - 07
✸€	07 - 09
♥♥	09 - 11
✸♥♥	11 - 13
✸♥	13 - 15
ø♥✈ϟ	15 - 17
€	17 - 19
♥	19 - 21
✈ø♥♥	21 - 23
♥	23 - 00

☲☳ 21-Gnawing And Chewing: Conquer difficulties with discipline and justice.

19SU

癸卯 Water Rabbit | *Metal* | ♓
Pleiades | Harvest | 5 - 7 - 7

✫ ♥€⏻ ✸✈

ø✸♥€	00 - 01
ø✸	01 - 03
	03 - 05
⏻✸	05 - 07
♥	07 - 09
♥✈⏻	09 - 11
€	11 - 13
♥	13 - 15
✈€	15 - 17
♥ϟ	17 - 19
ø♥	19 - 21
€✸♥	21 - 23
ø✸♥€	23 - 00

☱☳ 17-Following: Learn everything from the scratch and accept advice. This is the basis of authority and recognition.

-00:44 EOT 1:00:00 CEST/EDT	Year *Metal* Month *Water*	壬寅 Water Tiger Year 丙午 Fire Horse Month 壬寅 Planting of Grain

2022	**WEEK 25**	Water Tiger Year 5. Lunar Month 22. - 24. Day

20 MO

甲辰 Wood Dragon — *Fire* — ♓
Net — Opening — 5 - 7 - 8

✧✧⚡ ♥♥ ♥ ✈ ✸

♥	00 - 01
€♥♥⏻✹	01 - 03
✸✈€♥♥	03 - 05
∅✸♥♥♥	05 - 07
∅♥	07 - 09
✶€♥♥	09 - 11
✸♥♥	11 - 13
♥✹	13 - 15
✸€♥	15 - 17
♥	17 - 19
⚡	19 - 21
	21 - 23
♥	23 - 00

䷘ 25-Without Wrongdoing: Follow your intuition without calculating intention.

21 TU

乙巳 Wood Snake — *Fire* — 03:11 ☾ 03:42 ♈
Beak — Closing — 5 - 7 - 9/1

★★★ € ⏻ ♥♥ ✸
09:14 Summer Solstice

⏻✹	00 - 01
♥	01 - 03
✶∅€✸♥♥♥	03 - 05
✸♥♥	05 - 07
∅♥♥	07 - 09
∅	09 - 11
✸	11 - 13
✸	13 - 15
♥♥✹	15 - 17
	17 - 19
€♥♥	19 - 21
✈⚡	21 - 23
⏻✹	23 - 00

䷣ 36-Brightness Wounded: Hide your light under a bushel and persecute your aim.

22 WE

丙午 Fire Horse — *Water* — ♈
Orion — Establishment — 5 - 7 - 9

✧✧ ✹ ✈ €

♥♥€✹⚡	00 - 01
∅♥♥♥	01 - 03
✸♥	03 - 05
✸	05 - 07
✸	07 - 09
✸	09 - 11
∅♥	11 - 13
∅♥	13 - 15
✈♥♥	15 - 17
⏻✹	17 - 19
♥	19 - 21
✶€♥⏻✹	21 - 23
♥♥€✹⚡	23 - 00

䷕ 22-Adorning: Design everything functional and beautiful because beauty fosters function.

-01:35 EOT 1:00:00 CEST/EDT	Year *Metal* Month *Water*	壬寅 Water Tiger Year 丙午 Fire Horse Month 壬寅 Summer Solstice Jun 21 09:14

2022	**WEEK 25**	Water Tiger Year 5. Lunar Month 25. - 28. Day

23TH 丁未 Fire Goat — *Water* — 12:12 ♉
Well — Removal — 5 - 7 - 8
★★ ♥ ∅✈

♥♥	00 - 01
∅♥⚡	01 - 03
✺€♥	03 - 05
✺♥	05 - 07
	07 - 09
✈	09 - 11
€♥♥	11 - 13
€✺	13 - 15
✈€	15 - 17
♥✺	17 - 19
∅♥♥	19 - 21
⏻✺♥	21 - 23
♥	23 - 00

䷾ 63-Already Accomplished: An end is achieved. Finish accurately and prepare for the next begin.

24FR 戊申 Earth Monkey — *Earth* — ♉
Ghosts — Fulfillment — 5 - 7 - 7
★★⚡ ♥ € ⏻ ✈

✺♥	00 - 01
⏻♥	01 - 03
∅✺♥✈⚡	03 - 05
♥	05 - 07
€♥♥	07 - 09
✈∅♥	09 - 11
♥	11 - 13
✺	13 - 15
✺	15 - 17
€	17 - 19
✺	19 - 21
∅✺♥	21 - 23
✺♥	23 - 00

䷤ 37-Family: Be reliable and consolidate the output as a solid platform for further developments.

25SA 己酉 Earth Rooster — *Earth* — 23:26 ♊
Willow — Balance — 5 - 7 - 6
✈ ♥ ∅

⏻✺	00 - 01
∅♥	01 - 03
✈€♥	03 - 05
✺♥⚡	05 - 07
∅♥	07 - 09
	09 - 11
€	11 - 13
	13 - 15
⏻	15 - 17
∅✺♥	17 - 19
♥	19 - 21
€✈	21 - 23
♥⏻✺	23 - 00

䷶ 55-Overshadowing: Use your wealth with wisdom for your ambitions.

26SU 庚戌 Metal Dog — *Metal* — ♊
Star — Determination — 5 - 7 - 5
★★★ ♥

♥	00 - 01
€♥✺	01 - 03
✺♥	03 - 05
∅✺♥	05 - 07
⚡	07 - 09
	09 - 11
♥	11 - 13
♥♥	13 - 15
✺✈€	15 - 17
♥	17 - 19
✺♥	19 - 21
✈€	21 - 23
♥	23 - 00

䷝ 30-Brightness: Light your inner fire. Enlighten dark corners and unsettled affairs.

-02:14 EOT 1:00:00 CEST/EDT	Year *Metal* Month *Water*	壬寅 Water Tiger Year 丙午 Fire Horse Month 壬寅 Summer Solstice

June

2022	**WEEK 26**	Water Tiger Year 5. Lunar Month 29. - 30. Day Water Tiger Year 6. Lunar Month 1. Day

27 MO

辛亥 Metal Pig — *Metal* — ♊
Bow — Rigidity — 5 - 7 - 4

00 - 01
01 - 03
03 - 05
05 - 07
07 - 09
09 - 11
11 - 13
13 - 15
15 - 17
17 - 19
19 - 21
21 - 23
23 - 00

䷰ 49-Reforming: It is a convenient time for changes. Trust in your competence be persistent.

28 TU

壬子 Water Rat — *Wood* — 11:57 ♋
Wings — Destruction — 5 - 7 - 3

00 - 01
01 - 03
03 - 05
05 - 07
07 - 09
09 - 11
11 - 13
13 - 15
15 - 17
17 - 19
19 - 21
21 - 23
23 - 00

䷒ 19-Arriving: Seize the opportunity. Invest in your future.

29 WE

癸丑 Water Ox — *Wood* — 02:53 ● ♋
Carriage — Danger — 5 - 7 - 2

00 - 01
01 - 03
03 - 05
05 - 07
07 - 09
09 - 11
11 - 13
13 - 15
15 - 17
17 - 19
19 - 21
21 - 23
23 - 00

䷨ 41-Decreasing: Affiliate honesty with self-restraint. Small things provoke big ones.

-03:05 EOT 1:00:00 CEST/EDT	Year *Metal* Month *Water*	壬寅 Water Tiger Year 丙午 Fire Horse Month 壬寅 Summer Solstice

2022	WEEK **26**	Water Tiger Year 6. Lunar Month 2. - 5. Day

30TH

甲寅 Wood Tiger *Water* ♋
Horn Completion 5 - 7 - 1

★★★ ♥♥ ♥ € ⏻ ✈

✱♥♥	00 - 01
	01 - 03
€✱♥♥	03 - 05
♥	05 - 07
€	07 - 09
∅♥	09 - 11
✱♥	11 - 13
⏻✱	13 - 15
∅✱♥✈⚡	15 - 17
€	17 - 19
♥	19 - 21
✱∅€♥♥♥	21 - 23
✱♥♥	23 - 00

䷻ 60-Regulating: Identify your limitations. Extend suffocating ones, establish wise ones.

1FR

乙卯 Wood Rabbit *Water* 00:32 ♌
Neck Harvest 5 - 7 - 9

☆ ♥ € ⏻ ✱ ✱

♥	00 - 01
∅✱	01 - 03
	03 - 05
€✱	05 - 07
♥	07 - 09
✱♥✈	09 - 11
✱♥♥€	11 - 13
✱♥	13 - 15
✱€⏻✱	15 - 17
♥♥⚡	17 - 19
∅♥♥♥	19 - 21
€♥	21 - 23
♥	23 - 00

䷼ 61-Mutually Trusting: Have an open mind and search for the true core. This arises understanding, adjacency and continuance.

2SA

丙辰 Fire Dragon *Earth* ♌
Base Opening 5 - 7 - 8

★★★ ♥♥ ♥ ⏻ ✈

♥	00 - 01
€✱♥♥	01 - 03
✈	03 - 05
∅♥	05 - 07
∅✱♥	07 - 09
✱✱	09 - 11
♥♥	11 - 13
∅♥	13 - 15
€♥♥♥	15 - 17
⏻✱♥	17 - 19
⚡	19 - 21
⏻✱	21 - 23
♥	23 - 00

䷵ 54-The Libidinal Addiction: Be true to your emotions and addiction but with retention.

3SU

丁巳 Fire Snake *Earth* 12:16 ♍
House Closing 5 - 7 - 7

☆☆ € ⏻ ✱

✱	00 - 01
✱♥	01 - 03
✱∅€✱♥	03 - 05
€✱♥♥	05 - 07
∅	07 - 09
∅✱	09 - 11
€♥♥	11 - 13
	13 - 15
∅♥♥	15 - 17
⏻✱	17 - 19
€	19 - 21
✈⏻✱⚡	21 - 23
✱♥♥	23 - 00

䷥ 38-Misunderstanding:
Remain true to yourself. Develop individual differences to constructive connections.

-03:41 EOT 1:00:00 CEST/EDT	Year *Metal* Month *Water*	壬寅 Water Tiger Year 丙午 Fire Horse Month 壬寅 Summer Solstice

June

July

2022	**WEEK 27**	Water Tiger Year · 6. Lunar Month · 6. - 8. Day

4 MO

戊午 Earth Horse — *Fire* — ♍
Heart — Establishment — 5 - 7 - 6

☆̸☆̸ ✈ €̸

✸ ♥♥ € ϟ	00 - 01
♥	01 - 03
♥	03 - 05
♥♥ ✸	05 - 07
♥♥	07 - 09
	09 - 11
ø ♥	11 - 13
✸ ♥	13 - 15
✈	15 - 17
	17 - 19
✸ ♥	19 - 21
✈̸ €̸ ✸ ♥ ♥♥	21 - 23
✸ ♥♥ € ϟ	23 - 00

☱ 58-Pleasing: With an inner smile about yourself and the world you will win the hearts of other people and free your own.

5 TU

己未 Earth Goat — *Fire* — 22:11 ♎
Tail — Removal — 5 - 7 - 5

★★ ♥ ♥♥ ø ✈̸

♥ ⏻	00 - 01
ø ✸ ♥ ϟ	01 - 03
€ ✸ ♥♥	03 - 05
♥	05 - 07
	07 - 09
✈	09 - 11
€ ♥	11 - 13
€̸ ✸	13 - 15
✈̸ €̸ ⏻	15 - 17
ø ✸ ♥♥	17 - 19
ø ♥	19 - 21
♥	21 - 23
♥ ♥♥ ⏻	23 - 00

☰ 10-Treading: Show self-confidence and inner strength together with sereneness.

6 WE

庚申 Metal Monkey — *Wood* — ♎
Basket — Fulfillment — 5 - 7 - 4

☆̸ ϟ ♥ € ✈

✸ ♥	00 - 01
⏻	01 - 03
ø ♥ ✈ ϟ	03 - 05
♥	05 - 07
€ ♥	07 - 09
✈̸ ø €̸ ♥♥	09 - 11
♥♥	11 - 13
	13 - 15
€	15 - 17
€̸ ♥♥	17 - 19
♥♥	19 - 21
ø ♥ ♥♥	21 - 23
✸ ♥	23 - 00

☷ 11-Prominence: Work together and complement one another. Everyone will profit.

-04:26 EOT 1:00:00 CEST/EDT	Year *Metal* Month *Water*	壬寅 Water Tiger Year 丙午 Fire Horse Month 壬寅 Summer Solstice

2022	**WEEK 27**	Water Tiger Year 6. Lunar Month 9. - 12. Day

July

✱♥ 00 - 01	**7TH**	辛酉 Metal Rooster *Wood* 02:14 ☽ ♎
∅✱♥ 01 - 03		Dipper Balance / Fulfillment 5 - 7/6 - 3
✱€⏻✱ 03 - 05	☆	♥ ∅ until 02:39
♥ϟ 05 - 07	★★	♥ € ⏻ ✈ ♥ from 02:39
∅✱♥ 07 - 09		02:39 Slight Heat
09 - 11		
⏻€✱ 11 - 13		
✱ 13 - 15		
♥ 15 - 17		
∅♥€ 17 - 19		
♥♥ 19 - 21		
€✈ 21 - 23		
✱♥ 23 - 00	䷙	26-Great Gains: Focus your strength. Go out and utilize your capabilities profitably.

✱♥ 00 - 01	**8FR**	壬戌 Water Dog *Water* 05:10 ♏
∅€♥ 01 - 03		Ox Balance 5 - 6 - 2
✱♥ 03 - 05	☆☆	♥∅
♥ 05 - 07		
ϟ 07 - 09		
⏻✱ 09 - 11		
✱♥♥ 11 - 13		
∅♥✱ 13 - 15		
✈€ 15 - 17		
♥♥ 17 - 19		
✱ 19 - 21		
✱ 21 - 23		
✱♥ 23 - 00	䷄	5-Waiting: Be patient and pursue your goal, step by step.

✱€ 00 - 01	**9SA**	癸亥 Water Pig *Water* ♏
✱ 01 - 03		Maiden Determination 5 - 6 - 1
♥♥ 03 - 05	☆☆	✱✱
€⏻✱♥ 05 - 07		
✱♥ 07 - 09		
✈ϟ 09 - 11		
♥ 11 - 13		
♥ 13 - 15		
✱€♥♥ 15 - 17		
♥♥ 17 - 19		
∅€ 19 - 21		
∅✱♥ 21 - 23		
✱€ 23 - 00	䷈	9-Small Savings: Go for your ambition with small steps instead of great leaps.

€✱ 00 - 01	**10SU**	甲子 Wood Rat *Metal* 08:36 ♐
⏻✱♥ 01 - 03		Void Rigidity 5 - 6 - 9
✈€♥ 03 - 05	★★	✱ ⏻ ♥♥✱
∅♥ 05 - 07		
♥ 07 - 09		
✱€♥ 09 - 11		
✱♥ϟ 11 - 13		
♥♥✱ 13 - 15		
✱♥ 15 - 17		
♥ 17 - 19		
✱ 19 - 21		
✱♥ 21 - 23		
€✱ 23 - 00	䷡	34-Great Strength: Check your handling of power. Grandeur and justice belong together.

-04:56 EOT 1:00:00 CEST/EDT	Year *Metal* Month *Water*	壬寅 Water Tiger Year 丙午 Fire Horse Month 壬寅 Water Tiger Year 壬寅 Fire Goat Month Jul 07 02:39

2022	WEEK 28	Water Tiger Year 6. Lunar Month 13. - 15. Day

11 MO

乙丑 Wood Ox — *Metal* — ♐
Roof — Destruction — 5 - 6 - 8

00 - 01	
01 - 03	
03 - 05	
05 - 07	
07 - 09	
09 - 11	
11 - 13	
13 - 15	
15 - 17	
17 - 19	
19 - 21	
21 - 23	
23 - 00	

14-Great Reward: Use your capabilities and assets for common weal.

12 TU

丙寅 Fire Tiger — *Fire* — 09:02 ♑
Room — Danger — 5 - 6 - 7

★★

00 - 01	
01 - 03	
03 - 05	
05 - 07	
07 - 09	
09 - 11	
11 - 13	
13 - 15	
15 - 17	
17 - 19	
19 - 21	
21 - 23	
23 - 00	

43-Severing: Stand up frankly for your own truth. Be determined but not offending.

13 WE

丁卯 Fire Rabbit — *Fire* — 18:38 ○ — ♑
Wall — Completion — 5 - 6 - 6

★★

00 - 01	
01 - 03	
03 - 05	
05 - 07	
07 - 09	
09 - 11	
11 - 13	
13 - 15	
15 - 17	
17 - 19	
19 - 21	
21 - 23	
23 - 00	

44-Meeting: Examine a seductive offer with minuteness and hold off.

-05:31 EOT 1:00:00 CEST/EDT	Year *Metal* Month *Water*	壬寅 Water Tiger Year 丁未 Fire Goat Month 壬寅 Slight Heat

2022	**WEEK 28**	Water Tiger Year 6. Lunar Month 16. - 19. Day

July

✱♥ 00 - 01 €⏻ 01 - 03 ✈ 03 - 05 ∅♥♥✱ 05 - 07 ∅♥♥ 07 - 09 ✗ 09 - 11 ♥ 11 - 13 ♥✱ 13 - 15 €♥ 15 - 17 ♥ 17 - 19 ✱⚡ 19 - 21 ✱♥ 21 - 23 ✱♥ 23 - 00	14TH ☆☆	戊辰 Earth Dragon *Wood* 08:08 ♒ Astride Harvest 5 - 6 - 5 ♥ ♥ € ⏻ ✱ ✗ 28-Great Test: Do not blow your plans out of proportions. Be gentle and mind your balance.
⏻✱♥ 00 - 01 ♥ 01 - 03 ✗∅€♥✱ 03 - 05 €♥ 05 - 07 ∅ 07 - 09 ∅✱ 09 - 11 € 11 - 13 13 - 15 ♥ 15 - 17 ✱ 17 - 19 ✱€♥ 19 - 21 ✱✈⚡ 21 - 23 ⏻✱ 23 - 00	15FR ☆☆	己巳 Earth Snake *Wood* ♒ Rope Opening 5 - 6 - 4 ♥ ✈ ✱ 50-The Caldron: Sort out material and spiritual ballast and create free space for new ideas.
♥€⚡ 00 - 01 ♥♥✱ 01 - 03 ♥ 03 - 05 ♥ 05 - 07 07 - 09 € 09 - 11 ∅♥ 11 - 13 ♥ 13 - 15 ✱✈€ 15 - 17 ♥ 17 - 19 ✱♥♥ 19 - 21 ✗€✱♥ 21 - 23 ♥€⚡ 23 - 00	16SA ★	庚午 Metal Horse *Earth* 08:09 ♓ Stomach Closing 5 - 6 - 3 ♥ € ⏻ ✱ 32-Constancy: Take up a solid position without freezing.
♥♥ 00 - 01 ∅♥⚡ 01 - 03 ⏻€✱ 03 - 05 ♥ 05 - 07 ✱ 07 - 09 ✈ 09 - 11 ⏻✱♥ 11 - 13 € 13 - 15 ✗€♥ 15 - 17 ∅♥€ 17 - 19 ∅✱♥♥ 19 - 21 ✱♥ 21 - 23 ♥♥ 23 - 00	17SU ★	辛未 Metal Goat *Earth* ♓ Pleiades Establishment 5 - 6 - 2 ♥ ⏻ ✈ €
-05:53 EOT 1:00:00 CEST/EDT	Year *Metal* Month *Water*	壬寅 Water Tiger Year 丁未 Fire Goat Month 壬寅 Slight Heat

57-Penetrating: Get your goals clear and implement them, gentle but consequent.

2022	**WEEK 29**	Water Tiger Year 6. Lunar Month 20. - 22. Day

18 MO — 壬申 Water Monkey — *Metal* — 11:14 ♈
Net — Removal — 5 - 6 - 1

★★★ ϟ €̸ ⌀

♥	00 - 01
✹	01 - 03
⌀ ✸ ♥ ✈ ϟ	03 - 05
♥ ⏻	05 - 07
€ ♥	07 - 09
✈̸ €̸ ♥ ✹	09 - 11
✸	11 - 13
⌀ ✹ ♥	13 - 15
✹	15 - 17
€̸	17 - 19
✸	19 - 21
⌀ ✸ ♥ ♥ €	21 - 23
♥	23 - 00

☵ 48-The Well: Develop your potentials and take good care of yourself.

19 TU — 癸酉 Water Rooster — *Metal* — ♈
Beak — Fulfillment — 5 - 6 - 9

✈̸ ♥ € ✈ ♥ ✸

✸ ♥ €	00 - 01
⌀ ✸ ♥	01 - 03
✈̸ €̸	03 - 05
♥ ⏻ ✹ ϟ	05 - 07
⌀ ✹ ♥ ♥	07 - 09
⏻	09 - 11
€ ♥	11 - 13
	13 - 15
	15 - 17
⌀ ♥	17 - 19
♥ ♥	19 - 21
€̸ ✸ ✈	21 - 23
✸ ♥ €	23 - 00

☶ 18-Decaying: Do not be too good for humble work. Clear backlog.

20 WE — 甲戌 Wood Dog — *Fire* — 14:19 ☾ 18:33 ♉
Orion — Balance — 5 - 6 - 8

★★ ✹ ♥

♥	00 - 01
€̸ ♥ ✹	01 - 03
€ ♥ ♥	03 - 05
⌀ ♥	05 - 07
ϟ	07 - 09
♥	09 - 11
✸ ♥	11 - 13
♥ ♥ ✹	13 - 15
✸ ✈ €	15 - 17
♥ ♥	17 - 19
✹	19 - 21
✈̸ €̸	21 - 23
♥	23 - 00

☷ 46-Rising: Rely on your intuition. Put your plans into action - now.

-06:16 EOT 1:00:00 CEST/EDT	Year *Metal* Month *Water*	壬寅 Water Tiger Year 丁未 Fire Goat Month 壬寅 Slight Heat

2022	WEEK 29	Water Tiger Year 6. Lunar Month 23. - 26. Day

July

21TH

乙亥 Wood Pig — *Fire* — ♉

Well — Determination — 5 - 6 - 7

★★★

00 - 01
01 - 03
03 - 05
05 - 07
07 - 09
09 - 11
11 - 13
13 - 15
15 - 17
17 - 19
19 - 21
21 - 23
23 - 00

6-Litigating:
Be honest but not stubborn or impolite. Solve a conflict with empathy and compromising.

22FR

丙子 Fire Rat — *Water* — ♉

Ghosts — Rigidity — 5 - 6 - 6

★★★

20:08 Great Heat

00 - 01
01 - 03
03 - 05
05 - 07
07 - 09
09 - 11
11 - 13
13 - 15
15 - 17
17 - 19
19 - 21
21 - 23
23 - 00

47-Confining: Benefit from your problems for your progress but do not talk about it.

23SA

丁丑 Fire Ox — *Water* — 05:30 ♊

Willow — Destruction — 5 - 6 - 5

00 - 01
01 - 03
03 - 05
05 - 07
07 - 09
09 - 11
11 - 13
13 - 15
15 - 17
17 - 19
19 - 21
21 - 23
23 - 00

64-Not Yet Accomplished: Specify precisely what you want to start but finish it definitely.

24SU

戊寅 Earth Tiger — *Earth* — ♊

Star — Danger — 5 - 6 - 4

★★ €

00 - 01
01 - 03
03 - 05
05 - 07
07 - 09
09 - 11
11 - 13
13 - 15
15 - 17
17 - 19
19 - 21
21 - 23
23 - 00

40-Separating: Disengage yourself from dead weight and return to your roots. Complete necessary objectives immediately.

-06:27 EOT 1:00:00 CEST/EDT	Year *Metal* Month *Water*	壬寅 Water Tiger Year 丁未 Fire Goat Month 壬寅 Great Heat Jul 22 20:08

2022	WEEK 30	Water Tiger Year 6. Lunar Month 27. - 29. Day

25 MO — 己卯 Earth Rabbit — *Earth* — 18:09 ♋
Bow — Completion — 5 - 6 - 3
★★ ♥♥ ♥ € ⏻ ✈

♥✹♥	00 - 01
∅	01 - 03
✹♥	03 - 05
✹	05 - 07
♥♥	07 - 09
♥✈	09 - 11
♥€	11 - 13
♥	13 - 15
✈€⏻	15 - 17
✹♥ϟ	17 - 19
∅♥♥	19 - 21
€♥	21 - 23
♥✹	23 - 00

䷺ 59-Dispersing: Break deadlocked structures with changes and shared joy.

26 TU — 庚辰 Metal Dragon — *Metal* — ♋
Wings — Harvest — 5 - 6 - 2
☆☆ ♥♥ ♥ € ⏻ ✹ ✈

♥	00 - 01
€♥⏻✹	01 - 03
✈	03 - 05
∅♥♥	05 - 07
∅♥	07 - 09
✈€	09 - 11
♥	11 - 13
♥	13 - 15
✹€♥	15 - 17
✹♥♥	17 - 19
♥ϟ	19 - 21
	21 - 23
♥	23 - 00

䷜ 29-Cavern: Be truly and sincere to yourself. Overcome obstacles peacefully.

27 WE — 辛巳 Metal Snake — *Metal* — ♋
Carriage — Opening — 5 - 6 - 1
☆☆ ♥ ⏻ ✈ ✹

	00 - 01
♥	01 - 03
✈€♥♥✹	03 - 05
€♥	05 - 07
∅✹	07 - 09
∅	09 - 11
⏻✹	11 - 13
✹	13 - 15
∅✹	15 - 17
✹€	17 - 19
€	19 - 21
✈ϟ	21 - 23
	23 - 00

䷃ 4-Ignorance: Be enthusiastic and open minded but rely on your experience.

-06:34 EOT 1:00:00 CEST/EDT	Year *Metal* Month *Water*	壬寅 Water Tiger Year 丁未 Fire Goat Month 壬寅 Great Heat

2022	**WEEK 30**	Water Tiger Year Water Tiger Year	6. Lunar Month 7. Lunar Month	30. Day 1. - 3. Day

July

28TH

壬午 Water Horse — *Wood* — 17:55 ● 06:40 ♌

Horn — Closing — 5 - 6 - 9

★ 💕 ♥ € ⏻ ✸

💕€ϟ	00 - 01
∅💘💕✹	01 - 03
✸♥	03 - 05
💕⏻	05 - 07
	07 - 09
₠⏻✹	09 - 11
∅✸💘💕	11 - 13
∅✹♥💕	13 - 15
✸✈	15 - 17
✸	17 - 19
♥	19 - 21
✈̸💘	21 - 23
💕€ϟ	23 - 00

䷠ 33-Retiring: A retreat in the right moment saves your dignity. Be insistent.

29FR

癸未 Water Goat — *Wood* — ♌

Neck — Establishment — 5 - 6 - 8

★ ♥ ⏻ ✈ ✸ ₠

✸💘💕€	00 - 01
∅✸💘ϟ	01 - 03
€	03 - 05
⏻✹♥	05 - 07
✹💕	07 - 09
✈⏻	09 - 11
♥💕	11 - 13
₠✹	13 - 15
✈̸₠✸	15 - 17
∅✸💕	17 - 19
∅💘💕	19 - 21
✸♥	21 - 23
✸💘💕€	23 - 00

䷞ 31-Influencing:
Reconcile your ambitions and your needs. Use the natural power of attraction of all things.

30SA

甲申 Wood Monkey — *Water* — 18:04 ♍

Base — Removal — 5 - 6 - 7

★ϟ ✹ 💕₠

♥	00 - 01
⏻✹	01 - 03
∅💘✈€💕ϟ	03 - 05
💘	05 - 07
€♥	07 - 09
✈̸∅₠	09 - 11
✸💕	11 - 13
	13 - 15
	15 - 17
₠	17 - 19
	19 - 21
∅💘💕	21 - 23
♥	23 - 00

䷷ 56-Traveling: Scoop from your inner source, be attentive and start for new shore.

31SU

乙酉 Wood Rooster — *Water* — ♍

House — Fulfillment — 5 - 6 - 6

★★ ♥ € ✈ 💕

💕⏻✹	00 - 01
∅♥	01 - 03
✈̸₠	03 - 05
💕€ϟ	05 - 07
∅♥💕	07 - 09
✸	09 - 11
✸€	11 - 13
✸	13 - 15
⏻✹	15 - 17
∅💘	17 - 19
💘	19 - 21
₠✈	21 - 23
💕⏻✹	23 - 00

䷽ 62-Small Testing: Concentrate on the details and complete them with accuracy.

-06:33 EOT 1:00:00 CEST/EDT	Year *Metal* Month *Water*	壬寅 Water Tiger Year 丁未 Fire Goat Month 壬寅 Great Heat

August

2022	**WEEK 31**	Water Tiger Year 7. Lunar Month 4. - 6. Day

1 MO

丙戌 Fire Dog — *Earth* — ♍
Heart — Balance — 5 - 6 - 5

☆☆ ♥ø

♥✸	00 - 01
ø€♥	01 - 03
♥	03 - 05
ø♥♥	05 - 07
✸ϟ	07 - 09
✸€	09 - 11
✸♥	11 - 13
ø✸♥♥	13 - 15
✈€♥	15 - 17
♥♥⏻✸	17 - 19
✸	19 - 21
✈€⏻✸	21 - 23
♥✸	23 - 00

䷴ 53-Gradually Progressing: Achieve your plans, patient and with integrity.

2 TU

丁亥 Fire Pig — *Earth* — 03:52 ♎
Tail — Determination — 5 - 6 - 4

★★★ ✈

	00 - 01
	01 - 03
✸♥	03 - 05
€✸♥	05 - 07
	07 - 09
ø✈ϟ	09 - 11
✸€♥	11 - 13
✸♥	13 - 15
✈€♥♥	15 - 17
♥♥⏻✸	17 - 19
ø€	19 - 21
♥✸	21 - 23
♥	23 - 00

䷦ 39-Obstructing: Do not bash your head against a wall. Retreat, bethink and talk to friends.

3 WE

戊子 Earth Rat — *Fire* — ♎
Basket — Rigidity — 5 - 6 - 3

★★ ♥♥✈

€	00 - 01
⏻♥♥	01 - 03
✈	03 - 05
ø♥✸	05 - 07
♥♥	07 - 09
✈	09 - 11
✸♥ϟ	11 - 13
♥♥	13 - 15
♥	15 - 17
♥	17 - 19
✸	19 - 21
✸♥♥	21 - 23
€	23 - 00

䷳ 52-Stopping: Make peace with your core and do not get disturbed by emotions.

-06:23 EOT 1:00:00 CEST/EDT	Year *Metal* Month *Water*	壬寅 Water Tiger Year 丁未 Fire Goat Month 壬寅 Great Heat

2022	**WEEK 31**	Water Tiger Year 7. Lunar Month 7. - 10. Day

4TH

己丑 Earth Ox — *Fire* — 11:35 ♏
Dipper — Destruction — 5 - 6 - 2

☆⚡ ♥✸∅

⏻✸♥❤	00 - 01
♥✸	01 - 03
✗✸❤	03 - 05
❤	05 - 07
∅❤	07 - 09
♥	09 - 11
✸♥❤€	11 - 13
∅€✸♥⚡	13 - 15
⏻	15 - 17
∅✸♥	17 - 19
∅♥❤	19 - 21
✈	21 - 23
⏻✸♥	23 - 00

☷☶ 15-Modesty: Be modest but not humble or self-deprecating. Engage in common cause.

5FR

庚寅 Metal Tiger — *Wood* — 11:07 ☽ ♏
Ox — Danger — 5 - 6 - 1

★★ € ❤✸✗

❤	00 - 01
✸	01 - 03
✸	03 - 05
♥	05 - 07
€	07 - 09
∅♥❤	09 - 11
♥	11 - 13
⏻	13 - 15
∅✸♥✈€⚡	15 - 17
€❤	17 - 19
♥❤	19 - 21
✗∅€❤♥	21 - 23
❤	23 - 00

☰☷ 12-Adversity: Keep your balance and listen to your heart. Savor everyday commodities.

6SA

辛卯 Metal Rabbit — *Wood* — 16:35 ♐
Maiden — Completion — 5 - 6 - 9

★★★⚡ ❤♥€⏻✈

∅♥	00 - 01
∅	01 - 03
⏻✸	03 - 05
✸	05 - 07
✸♥❤	07 - 09
♥✈	09 - 11
❤⏻€	11 - 13
✸♥	13 - 15
✗€❤	15 - 17
❤€⚡	17 - 19
∅♥	19 - 21
€♥	21 - 23
∅♥	23 - 00

☱☷ 45-Gathering: Personal sacrifices foster your personal up growth.

7SU

壬辰 Water Dragon — *Water* — ♐
Void — Harvest / Completion — 5 - 6/5 - 8

★★ ❤♥€⏻ ✸✗ — until 12:30
★ ❤♥€⏻✈ — from 12:30
12:30 Coming of Autumn

♥	00 - 01
€❤✸	01 - 03
✸✈	03 - 05
♥❤	05 - 07
∅♥	07 - 09
✗€⏻✸	09 - 11
✸	11 - 13
∅♥❤	13 - 15
€♥	15 - 17
♥	17 - 19
⚡	19 - 21
€	21 - 23
♥	23 - 00

☲☷ 35-Promoting: Be upright, noble and generous. The lust for life evolves from good deeds.

-06:09 EOT 1:00:00 CEST/EDT	Year *Metal* Month *Water*	壬寅 Water Tiger Year 丁未 Fire Goat Month 壬寅 Water Tiger Year 壬申 Earth Monkey Month Aug 07 12:30

2022	**WEEK 32**	Water Tiger Year 7. Lunar Month 11. - 13. Day

8 MO

癸巳 Water Snake — *Water* — 18:43 ♑
Roof — Harvest — 5 - 5 - 7

★ ✈

✹ €	00 - 01
✹ ♥	01 - 03
✈ ∅ € ♥ ♥	03 - 05
€ ♥ ⏻ ✹	05 - 07
∅ ✹ ♥	07 - 09
	09 - 11
✹ ♥	11 - 13
✹	13 - 15
∅ ♥	15 - 17
	17 - 19
€	19 - 21
✹ ✈ ϟ	21 - 23
✹ €	23 - 00

☳☷ 16-Satisfying: Pass your enthusiasm to others. Together you will succeed faster.

9 TU

甲午 Wood Horse — *Metal* — ♑
Room — Opening — 5 - 5 - 6

★★ ♥ ✈

♥ € ϟ	00 - 01
♥ ♥ ✹	01 - 03
€ ♥ ♥	03 - 05
♥	05 - 07
✹	07 - 09
€ ✹ ♥	09 - 11
∅ ✹ ♥	11 - 13
✹ ♥	13 - 15
✹ ✈	15 - 17
	17 - 19
♥	19 - 21
✈ € ♥	21 - 23
♥ € ϟ	23 - 00

☴☷ 20-Observing: Take the time to take personal stock as a basis for your spiritual growth.

10 WE

乙未 Wood Goat — *Metal* — 18:47 ♒
Wall — Closing — 5 - 5 - 5

★ € ✹

♥ ♥ ⏻ ✹	00 - 01
∅ ♥ ϟ	01 - 03
€	03 - 05
€ ♥	05 - 07
✹ ♥	07 - 09
✹ ✈	09 - 11
✹ ♥	11 - 13
€	13 - 15
✈ € ⏻ ✹	15 - 17
∅ ♥	17 - 19
∅ ♥	19 - 21
♥	21 - 23
♥ ♥ ⏻ ✹	23 - 00

☵☷ 8-Alliance: Do not hesitate to act jointly.

-05:43 EOT 1:00:00 CEST/EDT	Year *Metal* Month *Earth*	壬寅 Water Tiger Year 戊申 Earth Monkey Month 壬寅 Coming of Autumn

2022	WEEK 32	Water Tiger Year 7. Lunar Month 14. - 17. Day

11TH

丙申 Fire Monkey — *Fire* — ♒

Astride — Establishment — 5 - 5 - 4

00 - 01
01 - 03
03 - 05
05 - 07
07 - 09
09 - 11
11 - 13
13 - 15
15 - 17
17 - 19
19 - 21
21 - 23
23 - 00

23-Stripping: Dark clouds are rising. Retreat and bethink yourself.

12FR

丁酉 Fire Rooster — *Fire* — 01:36 ○ 18:40 ♓

Rope — Removal — 5 - 5 - 3

00 - 01
01 - 03
03 - 05
05 - 07
07 - 09
09 - 11
11 - 13
13 - 15
15 - 17
17 - 19
19 - 21
21 - 23
23 - 00

24-Returning: Something re-enters your life. Clarify your ambitions to get a good start.

13SA

戊戌 Earth Dog — *Wood* — ♓

Stomach — Fulfillment — 5 - 5 - 2

00 - 01
01 - 03
03 - 05
05 - 07
07 - 09
09 - 11
11 - 13
13 - 15
15 - 17
17 - 19
19 - 21
21 - 23
23 - 00

27-Jaws: Take care of your corporal and mental nourishment.

14SU

己亥 Earth Pig — *Wood* — 20:35 ♈

Pleiades — Balance — 5 - 5 - 1

00 - 01
01 - 03
03 - 05
05 - 07
07 - 09
09 - 11
11 - 13
13 - 15
15 - 17
17 - 19
19 - 21
21 - 23
23 - 00

3-Accumulating: The start is difficult. Be patient and accept help. You will be successful.

-05:17 EOT 1:00:00 CEST/EDT	Year *Metal* Month *Earth*	壬寅 Water Tiger Year 戊申 Earth Monkey Month 壬寅 Coming of Autumn

August

2022	**WEEK 33**	Water Tiger Year 7. Lunar Month 18. - 20. Day

15 MO

庚子 Metal Rat — *Earth* — ♈
Net — Determination — 5 - 5 - 9

★★

€✸	00 - 01
⏻✸♥	01 - 03
✈	03 - 05
∅♥	05 - 07
✸♥	07 - 09
✈€✸	09 - 11
♥ϟ	11 - 13
♥♥	13 - 15
✸€♥	15 - 17
	17 - 19
♥	19 - 21
♥	21 - 23
€✸	23 - 00

☴☳ 42-Increasing: Use your abilities for common welfare. Learn from mistakes.

16 TU

辛丑 Metal Ox — *Earth* — ♈
Beak — Rigidity — 5 - 5 - 8

∅ € ♥∅✈

♥	00 - 01
♥✸	01 - 03
✈⏻✸	03 - 05
♥	05 - 07
∅✸♥	07 - 09
♥	09 - 11
♥♥⏻✸	11 - 13
∅€✸♥ϟ	13 - 15
♥	15 - 17
∅€♥	17 - 19
∅♥	19 - 21
✈	21 - 23
♥	23 - 00

☳☳ 51-Startling:
A change is imminent. Keep your calmness and humor, everything will turn to good account.

17 WE

壬寅 Water Tiger — *Metal* — 02:22 ♉
Orion — Destruction — 5 - 5 - 7

★ϟ ✈ ♥

♥	00 - 01
∅✸	01 - 03
	03 - 05
♥⏻	05 - 07
✸€	07 - 09
♥♥	09 - 11
✸♥♥	11 - 13
✸♥	13 - 15
∅♥✈ϟ	15 - 17
€	17 - 19
♥	19 - 21
✈∅♥♥	21 - 23
♥	23 - 00

☲☳ 21-Gnawing And Chewing: Conquer difficulties with discipline and justice.

-04:34 EOT 1:00:00 CEST/EDT	Year *Metal* Month *Earth*	壬寅 Water Tiger Year 戊申 Earth Monkey Month 壬寅 Coming of Autumn

18TH

癸卯 Water Rabbit *Metal* ♉
Well Danger 5 - 5 - 6

★★★ ⏻ ✗

∅✸❦€	00 - 01
∅✸	01 - 03
	03 - 05
⏻✸	05 - 07
❦	07 - 09
❦✈⏻	09 - 11
€	11 - 13
♥	13 - 15
✗€	15 - 17
❦⚡	17 - 19
∅♥	19 - 21
€✸♥	21 - 23
∅✸❦€	23 - 00

☱ 17-Following: Learn everything from the scratch and accept advice. This is the basis of authority and recognition.

19FR

甲辰 Wood Dragon *Fire* 04:36 ☾ 12:20 ♊
Ghosts Completion 5 - 5 - 5

✗✗ ❦ ♥ € ⏻ ✈

♥	00 - 01
€❦⏻✸	01 - 03
✸✈€❦	03 - 05
∅✸❦❦	05 - 07
∅❦	07 - 09
✗€❦	09 - 11
✸❦	11 - 13
❦✸	13 - 15
✸€♥	15 - 17
♥	17 - 19
⚡	19 - 21
	21 - 23
♥	23 - 00

☰ 25-Without Wrongdoing: Follow your intuition without calculating intention.

20SA

乙巳 Wood Snake *Fire* ♊
Willow Harvest 5 - 5 - 4

★ ✸✗

⏻✸	00 - 01
♥	01 - 03
✗∅€✸❦❦	03 - 05
✸❦	05 - 07
∅❦	07 - 09
∅	09 - 11
✸	11 - 13
✸	13 - 15
❦✸	15 - 17
	17 - 19
€❦	19 - 21
✈⚡	21 - 23
⏻✸	23 - 00

☷ 36-Brightness Wounded: Hide your light under a bushel and persecute your aim.

21SU

丙午 Fire Horse *Water* ♊
Star Opening 5 - 5 - 3

★★★ ♥ ✈

❦€✸⚡	00 - 01
∅❦❦	01 - 03
✸♥	03 - 05
✸	05 - 07
✸	07 - 09
✸	09 - 11
∅❦	11 - 13
∅♥	13 - 15
✈❦	15 - 17
⏻✸	17 - 19
♥	19 - 21
✗€❦⏻✸	21 - 23
❦€✸⚡	23 - 00

☶ 22-Adorning: Design everything functional and beautiful because beauty fosters function.

-03:57 EOT
1:00:00 CEST/EDT

Year *Metal*
Month *Earth*

壬寅 Water Tiger Year 戊申 Earth Monkey Month
壬寅 Coming of Autumn

2022	**WEEK 34**	Water Tiger Year 7. Lunar Month 25. - 27. Day

22 MO

丁未 Fire Goat — *Water* — 00:50 ♋
Bow — Closing — 5 - 5 - 2

★★ ♥ € ✸

♥♥	00 - 01
Ø♥ϟ	01 - 03
✸€♥	03 - 05
✸♥	05 - 07
	07 - 09
✈	09 - 11
€♥♥	11 - 13
€̸✸	13 - 15
✈̸€̸	15 - 17
♥✸	17 - 19
Ø♥♥	19 - 21
⏻✸♥	21 - 23
♥	23 - 00

䷾ 63-Already Accomplished: An end is achieved. Finish accurately and prepare for the next begin.

23 TU

戊申 Earth Monkey — *Earth* — ♋
Wings — Establishment — 5 - 5 - 1

★★★ϟ ♥ ⏻ ✈ €̸
03:17 Limit of Heat

✸♥	00 - 01
⏻♥	01 - 03
Ø✸♥✈ϟ	03 - 05
♥	05 - 07
€♥♥	07 - 09
✈̸Ø♥	09 - 11
♥	11 - 13
✸	13 - 15
✸	15 - 17
€̸	17 - 19
✸	19 - 21
Ø✸♥	21 - 23
✸♥	23 - 00

䷤ 37-Family: Be reliable and consolidate the output as a solid platform for further developments.

24 WE

己酉 Earth Rooster — *Earth* — 13:25 ♌
Carriage — Removal — 5 - 5 - 9

☆̸☆̸ ♥ Ø ✈̸

⏻✸	00 - 01
Ø♥	01 - 03
✈̸€̸♥	03 - 05
✸♥ϟ	05 - 07
Ø♥	07 - 09
	09 - 11
€	11 - 13
	13 - 15
⏻	15 - 17
Ø✸♥	17 - 19
♥	19 - 21
€̸✈	21 - 23
♥⏻✸	23 - 00

䷶ 55-Overshadowing: Use your wealth with wisdom for your ambitions.

-03:00 EOT 1:00:00 CEST/EDT	Year *Metal* Month *Earth*	壬寅 Water Tiger Year 戊申 Earth Monkey Month 壬寅 Limit of Heat Aug 23 03:17

2022	WEEK 34	Water Tiger Year · 7. Lunar Month · 28. - 29. Day Water Tiger Year · 8. Lunar Month · 1. - 2. Day

25TH

庚戌 Metal Dog — *Metal* — ♌

Horn — Fulfillment — 5 - 5 - 8

★ ♥ € ✈

💞	00 - 01
€̸ 💘 ✹	01 - 03
✹̸ ♥	03 - 05
∅ ✹̸ ♥	05 - 07
ϟ	07 - 09
	09 - 11
♥	11 - 13
💘 💞	13 - 15
✹̸ ✈ €	15 - 17
💘	17 - 19
✹ 💞	19 - 21
✈̸ €̸	21 - 23
💞	23 - 00

䷝ 30-Brightness: Light your inner fire. Enlighten dark corners and unsettled affairs.

26FR

辛亥 Metal Pig — *Metal* — ♌

Neck — Balance — 5 - 5 - 7

☆̸ 💘 ∅ ✈̸

	00 - 01
	01 - 03
💞 ⏻ ♥	03 - 05
€̸ ✹̸ ♥	05 - 07
✹̸	07 - 09
∅ ✈ ϟ	09 - 11
⏻ ✹	11 - 13
✹̸ ♥	13 - 15
✈̸ €̸ 💘	15 - 17
💘 💞 €	17 - 19
∅ €	19 - 21
∅ 💘	21 - 23
	23 - 00

䷰ 49-Reforming: It is a convenient time for changes. Trust in your competence be persistent.

27SA

壬子 Water Rat — *Wood* — 08:16 ● 00:31 ♍

Base — Determination — 5 - 5 - 6

☆̸☆̸ ✹ ⏻

€ ✹	00 - 01
✹ ♥	01 - 03
✹̸ ✈	03 - 05
💘	05 - 07
♥	07 - 09
✈̸ €̸ ⏻ ✹	09 - 11
✹̸ ϟ	11 - 13
∅ 💘 ✹	13 - 15
♥	15 - 17
💞	17 - 19
	19 - 21
💘 €	21 - 23
€ ✹	23 - 00

䷒ 19-Arriving: Seize the opportunity. Invest in your future.

28SU

癸丑 Water Ox — *Wood* — ♍

House — Rigidity — 5 - 5 - 5

☆̸☆̸ ✹ € ✈̸

✹̸ € ♥	00 - 01
💘	01 - 03
✈̸ ✹̸	03 - 05
💞 ⏻	05 - 07
∅ ✹	07 - 09
⏻ ♥	09 - 11
💘	11 - 13
∅ €̸ 💘 ϟ	13 - 15
	15 - 17
∅ ♥	17 - 19
∅ 💘	19 - 21
✹̸ ✈	21 - 23
✹̸ € ♥	23 - 00

䷨ 41-Decreasing: Affiliate honesty with self-restraint. Small things provoke big ones.

-02:12 EOT 1:00:00 CEST/EDT	Year *Metal* Month *Earth*	壬寅 Water Tiger Year 戊申 Earth Monkey Month 壬寅 Limit of Heat

2022	WEEK 35	Water Tiger Year 8. Lunar Month 3. - 5. Day

29 MO

甲寅 Wood Tiger — *Water* — 09:41 ♎
Heart — Destruction — 5 - 5 - 4

✯✯ϟ ✈ ❥✸⌀

✸❦	00 - 01
	01 - 03
€✸❦	03 - 05
❥	05 - 07
€	07 - 09
⌀❥	09 - 11
✸♥	11 - 13
⏻✸	13 - 15
⌀✸❥✈ϟ	15 - 17
₠	17 - 19
♥	19 - 21
⚹⌀₠❦♥	21 - 23
✸❦	23 - 00

䷻ 60-Regulating: Identify your limitations. Extend suffocating ones, establish wise ones.

30 TU

乙卯 Wood Rabbit — *Water* — ♎
Tail — Danger — 5 - 5 - 3

✯✯ ❦✸⚹

❥	00 - 01
⌀✸	01 - 03
	03 - 05
€✸	05 - 07
❥	07 - 09
✸❥✈	09 - 11
✸❦€	11 - 13
✸♥	13 - 15
⚹₠⏻✸	15 - 17
❦ϟ	17 - 19
⌀♥❦	19 - 21
₠♥	21 - 23
❥	23 - 00

䷼ 61-Mutually Trusting: Have an open mind and search for the true core. This arises understanding, adjacency and continuance.

31 WE

丙辰 Fire Dragon — *Earth* — 17:00 ♏
Basket — Completion — 5 - 5 - 2

★ ❦♥€⏻✈

♥	00 - 01
₠✸❦	01 - 03
✈	03 - 05
⌀❥	05 - 07
⌀✸❥	07 - 09
⚹✸	09 - 11
❦	11 - 13
⌀❥	13 - 15
€♥❦	15 - 17
⏻✸♥	17 - 19
ϟ	19 - 21
⏻✸	21 - 23
♥	23 - 00

䷵ 54-The Libidinal Addiction: Be true to your emotions and addiction but with retention.

-01:04 EOT 1:00:00 CEST/EDT	Year *Metal* Month *Earth*	壬寅 Water Tiger Year 戊申 Earth Monkey Month 壬寅 Limit of Heat

2022	**WEEK 35**	Water Tiger Year 8. Lunar Month 6. - 9. Day

1 TH

丁巳 Fire Snake *Earth* ♏

Dipper Harvest 5 - 5 - 1

✫✫ ✸✱

✸	00 - 01
✸♥	01 - 03
✱⌀₠✸❥	03 - 05
₠✸❣	05 - 07
⌀	07 - 09
⌀✹	09 - 11
€❣	11 - 13
	13 - 15
⌀❣	15 - 17
⏻✹	17 - 19
€	19 - 21
✈⏻✹ϟ	21 - 23
✸❣	23 - 00

䷥ 38-Misunderstanding:
Remain true to yourself. Develop individual differences to constructive connections.

2 FR

戊午 Earth Horse *Fire* 22:30 ♐

Ox Opening 5 - 5 - 9

★★★ ♥✈

✸❣€ϟ	00 - 01
❥	01 - 03
♥	03 - 05
❣✹	05 - 07
❣	07 - 09
	09 - 11
⌀❥	11 - 13
✹♥	13 - 15
✈	15 - 17
	17 - 19
✸♥	19 - 21
✱₠✸❥❣	21 - 23
✸❣€ϟ	23 - 00

䷹ 58-Pleasing: With an inner smile about yourself and the world you will win the hearts of other people and free your own.

3 SA

己未 Earth Goat *Fire* 18:08 ☽ ♐

Maiden Closing 5 - 5 - 8

★★★ € ✸

❥⏻	00 - 01
⌀✸❥ϟ	01 - 03
€✹❣	03 - 05
♥	05 - 07
	07 - 09
✈	09 - 11
€♥	11 - 13
₠✹	13 - 15
✱₠⏻	15 - 17
⌀✸❣	17 - 19
⌀❥	19 - 21
♥	21 - 23
❥❣⏻	23 - 00

䷉ 10-Treading: Show self-confidence and inner strength together with sereneness.

4 SU

庚申 Metal Monkey *Wood* ♐

Void Establishment 5 - 5 - 7

✫✫ϟ ♥⏻✈ ₠

✸♥	00 - 01
⏻	01 - 03
⌀❥✈ϟ	03 - 05
❥	05 - 07
€♥	07 - 09
✱⌀₠❣	09 - 11
❣	11 - 13
	13 - 15
€	15 - 17
₠❣	17 - 19
❣	19 - 21
⌀❥❣	21 - 23
✸♥	23 - 00

䷊ 11-Prominence: Work together and complement one another. Everyone will profit.

-00:09 EOT 1:00:00 CEST/EDT	Year *Metal* Month *Earth*	壬寅 Water Tiger Year 戊申 Earth Monkey Month 壬寅 Limit of Heat

September

September

2022	**WEEK 36**	Water Tiger Year 8. Lunar Month 10. - 12. Day

5 MO — 辛酉 Metal Rooster — *Wood* — 02:03 ♑
Roof — Removal — 5 - 5 - 6

✈✈ ♥Ø✈

✹♥	00 - 01
Ø✹♥	01 - 03
✈€⏻✹	03 - 05
♥ϟ	05 - 07
Ø✹♥	07 - 09
	09 - 11
⏻€✹	11 - 13
✹	13 - 15
♥	15 - 17
Ø♥€	17 - 19
♥♥	19 - 21
€✈	21 - 23
✹♥	23 - 00

26-Great Gains: Focus your strength. Go out and utilize your capabilities profitably.

6 TU — 壬戌 Water Dog — *Water* — ♑
Room — Fulfillment — 5 - 5 - 5

✈✈ ♥ ✹ € ⏻ ✈

✹♥	00 - 01
Ø€♥	01 - 03
✹♥	03 - 05
♥	05 - 07
ϟ	07 - 09
⏻✹	09 - 11
✹♥♥	11 - 13
Ø♥✹	13 - 15
✈€	15 - 17
♥♥	17 - 19
✹	19 - 21
✈	21 - 23
✹♥	23 - 00

5-Waiting: Be patient and pursue your goal, step by step.

7 WE — 癸亥 Water Pig — *Water* — 03:48 ♒
Wall — Balance / Fulfillment — 5 - 5/4 - 4

✈ ✹ ♥✈ — until 15:33
✈✈ ♥⏻ ♥ — from 15:33
15:33 White Dew

✹€	00 - 01
✹	01 - 03
♥♥	03 - 05
€⏻✹♥	05 - 07
✹♥	07 - 09
✈ϟ	09 - 11
♥	11 - 13
♥	13 - 15
✈€♥♥	15 - 17
♥♥	17 - 19
Ø€	19 - 21
Ø✹♥	21 - 23
✹€	23 - 00

9-Small Savings: Go for your ambition with small steps instead of great leaps.

01:09 EOT 1:00:00 CEST/EDT	Year *Metal* Month *Earth*	壬寅 Water Tiger Year 戊申 Earth Monkey Month 壬寅 Water Tiger Year 壬寅 Earth Rooster Month Sep 07 15:33

2022	**WEEK 36**	Water Tiger Year 8. Lunar Month 13. - 16. Day

8TH

甲子 Wood Rat — *Metal* — ♒
Astride — Balance — 5 - 4 - 3

€✸	00 - 01
⏻✸♥	01 - 03
✢€♥	03 - 05
∅♥	05 - 07
♥	07 - 09
✶€♥	09 - 11
✸♥ϟ	11 - 13
♥♥✸	13 - 15
✸♥	15 - 17
♥	17 - 19
✸	19 - 21
✸♥	21 - 23
€✸	23 - 00

34-Great Strength: Check your handling of power. Grandeur and justice belong together.

9FR

乙丑 Wood Ox — *Metal* — 04:45 ♓
Rope — Determination — 5 - 4 - 2

★★ ♥ € ∅

⏻✸♥	00 - 01
♥✸	01 - 03
✶	03 - 05
♥€	05 - 07
∅	07 - 09
✸♥	09 - 11
✸♥♥	11 - 13
∅€✸♥ϟ	13 - 15
⏻✸	15 - 17
∅♥	17 - 19
∅✸♥♥	19 - 21
✸✢	21 - 23
⏻✸♥	23 - 00

14-Great Reward: Use your capabilities and assets for common weal.

10SA

丙寅 Fire Tiger — *Fire* — 09:58 ○ — ♓
Stomach — Rigidity — 5 - 4 - 1

★★ ⏻ ♥€✶

♥✸	00 - 01
∅	01 - 03
✸	03 - 05
♥♥	05 - 07
✸€	07 - 09
∅✸♥♥€	09 - 11
♥	11 - 13
	13 - 15
∅♥✢♥ϟ	15 - 17
€⏻✸	17 - 19
✸♥	19 - 21
✶€♥♥	21 - 23
♥✸	23 - 00

43-Severing: Stand up frankly for your own truth. Be determined but not offending.

11SU

丁卯 Fire Rabbit — *Fire* — 06:42 ♈
Pleiades — Destruction — 5 - 4 - 9

ϟ ♥✸

∅♥	00 - 01
∅	01 - 03
✸♥	03 - 05
	05 - 07
♥♥	07 - 09
♥✢	09 - 11
€	11 - 13
♥	13 - 15
✶€	15 - 17
♥⏻✸ϟ	17 - 19
∅✸♥	19 - 21
€⏻♥	21 - 23
∅♥♥	23 - 00

44-Meeting: Examine a seductive offer with minuteness and hold off.

02:10 EOT 1:00:00 CEST/EDT	Year *Metal* Month *Earth*	壬寅 Water Tiger Year 己酉 Earth Rooster Month 壬寅 White Dew

2022	**WEEK 37**	Water Tiger Year 8. Lunar Month 17. - 19. Day

12 MO

戊辰 Earth Dragon *Wood* ♈
Net Danger 5 - 4 - 8

☆☆ ♥ € ❦ ✸ ∅ ✈

✸♥	00 - 01
€⏻	01 - 03
✈	03 - 05
∅♥❦✸	05 - 07
∅♥❦	07 - 09
✈	09 - 11
❦	11 - 13
♥✸	13 - 15
€♥	15 - 17
♥	17 - 19
✸ϟ	19 - 21
✸❦	21 - 23
✸♥	23 - 00

䷛ 28-Great Test: Do not blow your plans out of proportions. Be gentle and mind your balance.

13 TU

己巳 Earth Snake *Wood* 11:32 ♉
Beak Completion 5 - 4 - 7

★★★ ♥ € ⏻ ✈

⏻✸❦	00 - 01
♥	01 - 03
✈∅€♥✸	03 - 05
€❦	05 - 07
∅	07 - 09
∅✸	09 - 11
€	11 - 13
	13 - 15
❦	15 - 17
✸	17 - 19
✸€❦	19 - 21
✸✈ϟ	21 - 23
⏻✸	23 - 00

䷱ 50-The Caldron: Sort out material and spiritual ballast and create free space for new ideas.

14 WE

庚午 Metal Horse *Earth* ♉
Orion Harvest 5 - 4 - 6

☆☆ ❦ ♥ ✸ € ⏻ ✈

❦€ϟ	00 - 01
♥❦✸	01 - 03
♥	03 - 05
❦	05 - 07
	07 - 09
€	09 - 11
∅♥	11 - 13
♥	13 - 15
✸✈€	15 - 17
❦	17 - 19
✸♥❦	19 - 21
✈€✸♥	21 - 23
❦€ϟ	23 - 00

䷟ 32-Constancy: Take up a solid position without freezing.

03:33 EOT 1:00:00 CEST/EDT	Year *Metal* Month *Earth*	壬寅 Water Tiger Year 己酉 Earth Rooster Month 壬寅 White Dew

2022	WEEK **37**	Water Tiger Year 8. Lunar Month 20. - 23. Day

September

15TH

辛未 Metal Goat — *Earth* — 20:17 ♊
Well — Opening — 5 - 4 - 5

★ 💕♥€✈

❥💕	00 - 01
⏻̸❥⚡	01 - 03
⏻€✺	03 - 05
♥	05 - 07
✹	07 - 09
✈	09 - 11
⏻✺♥	11 - 13
€̸	13 - 15
✈̸€̸💕	15 - 17
⏻̸💕€	17 - 19
⏻̸✹❥💕	19 - 21
✹♥	21 - 23
❥💕	23 - 00

䷸ 57-Penetrating: Get your goals clear and implement them, gentle but consequent.

16FR

壬申 Water Monkey — *Metal* — ♊
Ghosts — Closing — 5 - 4 - 4

★★⚡ ⏻✈ ✹

♥	00 - 01
✺	01 - 03
⏻̸✹❥✈⚡	03 - 05
❥⏻	05 - 07
€♥	07 - 09
✈̸€̸💕✺	09 - 11
✹	11 - 13
⏻̸✺💕	13 - 15
✺	15 - 17
€̸	17 - 19
✹	19 - 21
⏻̸✹❥💕€	21 - 23
♥	23 - 00

䷯ 48-The Well: Develop your potentials and take good care of yourself.

17SA

癸酉 Water Rooster — *Metal* — 21:52 ☾ — ♊
Willow — Establishment — 5 - 4 - 3

☆̸☆̸ ✈ €̸

✹💕€	00 - 01
⏻̸✹♥	01 - 03
✈̸€̸	03 - 05
💕⏻✺⚡	05 - 07
⏻̸✺♥💕	07 - 09
⏻	09 - 11
€💕	11 - 13
	13 - 15
	15 - 17
⏻̸❥	17 - 19
❥💕	19 - 21
€̸✹✈	21 - 23
✹💕€	23 - 00

䷑ 18-Decaying: Do not be too good for humble work. Clear backlog.

18SU

甲戌 Wood Dog — *Fire* — 08:12 ♋
Star — Removal — 5 - 4 - 2

★★ € ❥⏻̸✈̸

💕	00 - 01
€̸❥✺	01 - 03
€♥💕	03 - 05
⏻̸♥	05 - 07
⚡	07 - 09
💕	09 - 11
✹♥	11 - 13
❥💕✺	13 - 15
✹✈€	15 - 17
❥💕	17 - 19
✺	19 - 21
✈̸€̸	21 - 23
💕	23 - 00

䷭ 46-Rising: Rely on your intuition. Put your plans into action - now.

04:37 EOT 1:00:00 CEST/EDT	Year *Metal* Month *Earth*	壬寅 Water Tiger Year 己酉 Earth Rooster Month 壬寅 White Dew

September

2022	WEEK 38	Water Tiger Year 8. Lunar Month 24. - 26. Day

19 MO — 乙亥 Wood Pig — *Fire* — ♋
Bow — Fulfillment — 5 - 4 - 1
★★★ ♥

⏻✸	00 - 01
	01 - 03
♥	03 - 05
♥	05 - 07
	07 - 09
∅ ⚡	09 - 11
	11 - 13
♥	13 - 15
€ ⏻	15 - 17
	17 - 19
∅€	19 - 21
∅	21 - 23
⏻✸	23 - 00

6-Litigating:
Be honest but not stubborn or impolite. Solve a conflict with empathy and compromising.

20 TU — 丙子 Fire Rat — *Water* — 20:54 ♌
Wings — Balance — 5 - 4 - 9
★★★ ∅

€✸	00 - 01
♥	01 - 03
	03 - 05
∅	05 - 07
♥	07 - 09
	09 - 11
⚡	11 - 13
∅	13 - 15
♥	15 - 17
⏻	17 - 19
	19 - 21
⏻✸	21 - 23
€✸	23 - 00

47-Confining: Benefit from your problems for your progress but do not talk about it.

21 WE — 丁丑 Fire Ox — *Water* — ♌
Carriage — Determination — 5 - 4 - 8
★★ € ∅

♥	00 - 01
✸	01 - 03
	03 - 05
	05 - 07
∅	07 - 09
♥	09 - 11
€	11 - 13
∅€⚡	13 - 15
	15 - 17
♥	17 - 19
∅	19 - 21
⏻✸	21 - 23
♥	23 - 00

64-Not Yet Accomplished: Specify precisely what you want to start but finish it definitely.

06:02 EOT 1:00:00 CEST/EDT	Year *Metal* Month *Earth*	壬寅 Water Tiger Year 己酉 Earth Rooster Month 壬寅 White Dew

2022	WEEK 38	Water Tiger Year 8. Lunar Month 27. - 30. Day

22 TH

戊寅 Earth Tiger — *Earth* — ♌
Horn — Rigidity — 5 - 4 - 7

00 - 01
01 - 03
03 - 05
05 - 07
07 - 09
09 - 11
11 - 13
13 - 15
15 - 17
17 - 19
19 - 21
21 - 23
23 - 00

40-Separating: Disengage yourself from dead weight and return to your roots. Complete necessary objectives immediately.

23 FR

己卯 Earth Rabbit — *Earth* — 08:08 ♍
Neck — Destruction — 5 - 4 - 6

01:04 Autumn Equinox

00 - 01
01 - 03
03 - 05
05 - 07
07 - 09
09 - 11
11 - 13
13 - 15
15 - 17
17 - 19
19 - 21
21 - 23
23 - 00

59-Dispersing: Break deadlocked structures with changes and shared joy.

24 SA

庚辰 Metal Dragon — *Metal* — ♍
Base — Danger — 5 - 4 - 5

00 - 01
01 - 03
03 - 05
05 - 07
07 - 09
09 - 11
11 - 13
13 - 15
15 - 17
17 - 19
19 - 21
21 - 23
23 - 00

29-Cavern: Be truly and sincere to yourself. Overcome obstacles peacefully.

25 SU

辛巳 Metal Snake — *Metal* — 21:54 ● 16:52 ♎
House — Completion — 5 - 4 - 4

00 - 01
01 - 03
03 - 05
05 - 07
07 - 09
09 - 11
11 - 13
13 - 15
15 - 17
17 - 19
19 - 21
21 - 23
23 - 00

4-Ignorance: Be enthusiastic and open minded but rely on your experience.

07:06 EOT 1:00:00 CEST/EDT	Year *Metal* Month *Earth*	壬寅 Water Tiger Year 己酉 Earth Rooster Month 壬寅 Autumn Equinox Sep 23 01:04

September

September

2022	WEEK 39	Water Tiger Year 9. Lunar Month 1. - 3. Day

26 MO

壬午 Water Horse — *Wood* — ♎
Heart — Harvest — 5 - 4 - 3

★★★ ♥♥ € ⏻ ✈

♥ € ⚡	00 - 01
⌀ ♥ ♥ ✱	01 - 03
✱ ♥	03 - 05
♥ ⏻	05 - 07
	07 - 09
€ ⏻ ✱	09 - 11
⌀ ✱ ♥ ♥	11 - 13
⌀ ✱ ♥ ♥	13 - 15
✱ ✈	15 - 17
✱	17 - 19
♥	19 - 21
✈ ♥	21 - 23
♥ € ⚡	23 - 00

33-Retiring: A retreat in the right moment saves your dignity. Be insistent.

27 TU

癸未 Water Goat — *Wood* — 23:13 ♏
Tail — Opening — 5 - 4 - 2

★ ♥ ♥ € ⏻ ✈

✱ ♥ ♥ €	00 - 01
⌀ ✱ ♥ ⚡	01 - 03
€	03 - 05
⏻ ✱ ♥	05 - 07
✱ ♥	07 - 09
✈ ⏻	09 - 11
♥ ♥	11 - 13
€ ✱	13 - 15
✈ € ✱	15 - 17
⌀ ✱ ♥	17 - 19
⌀ ♥ ♥	19 - 21
✱ ♥	21 - 23
✱ ♥ ♥ €	23 - 00

31-Influencing:
Reconcile your ambitions and your needs. Use the natural power of attraction of all things.

28 WE

甲申 Wood Monkey — *Water* — ♏
Basket — Closing — 5 - 4 - 1

★★ ⚡ ♥ ⏻ ✈ ✱

♥	00 - 01
⏻ ✱	01 - 03
⌀ ♥ ✈ € ♥ ⚡	03 - 05
♥	05 - 07
€ ♥	07 - 09
✈ ⌀ €	09 - 11
✱ ♥	11 - 13
	13 - 15
	15 - 17
€	17 - 19
	19 - 21
⌀ ♥ ♥	21 - 23
♥	23 - 00

56-Traveling: Scoop from your inner source, be attentive and start for new shore.

08:29 EOT 1:00:00 CEST/EDT	Year *Metal* Month *Earth*	壬寅 Water Tiger Year 己酉 Earth Rooster Month 壬寅 Autumn Equinox

2022	**WEEK 39**	Water Tiger Year 9. Lunar Month 4. - 7. Day

29TH

乙酉 Wood Rooster *Water* ♏

Dipper Establishment 5 - 4 - 9

☆̸☆̸ ✈ €̸

💞⏻✹	00 - 01
⌀♥	01 - 03
✈̸€̸	03 - 05
💞€ϟ	05 - 07
⌀♥💕	07 - 09
✸	09 - 11
✸€	11 - 13
✸	13 - 15
⏻✹	15 - 17
⌀❥	17 - 19
❥	19 - 21
€̸✈	21 - 23
💞⏻✹	23 - 00

䷽ 62-Small Testing: Concentrate on the details and complete them with accuracy.

30FR

丙戌 Fire Dog *Earth* 03:54 ♐

Ox Removal 5 - 4 - 8

☆̸☆̸ € 💞❥⌀✈̸

💞✹	00 - 01
⌀€̸❥	01 - 03
♥	03 - 05
⌀♥💕	05 - 07
✸ϟ	07 - 09
✸€	09 - 11
✸♥	11 - 13
⌀✸❥💞	13 - 15
✈€💕	15 - 17
❥💞⏻✹	17 - 19
✹	19 - 21
✈̸€̸⏻✹	21 - 23
💞✹	23 - 00

䷴ 53-Gradually Progressing: Achieve your plans, patient and with integrity.

1SA

丁亥 Fire Pig *Earth* ♐

Maiden Fulfillment 5 - 4 - 7

★★★ ♥

	00 - 01
	01 - 03
✸♥	03 - 05
€̸✸♥	05 - 07
	07 - 09
⌀✈ϟ	09 - 11
✸€💕	11 - 13
✸♥	13 - 15
✈̸€̸❥💞	15 - 17
❥💞⏻✹	17 - 19
⌀€	19 - 21
❥✹	21 - 23
💕	23 - 00

䷦ 39-Obstructing: Do not bash your head against a wall. Retreat, bethink and talk to friends.

2SU

戊子 Earth Rat *Fire* 07:32 ♑

Void Balance 5 - 4 - 6

★★ ⌀

€	00 - 01
⏻♥💕	01 - 03
✈	03 - 05
⌀❥✹	05 - 07
♥💕	07 - 09
✈̸	09 - 11
✸💞ϟ	11 - 13
❥💞	13 - 15
♥	15 - 17
💞	17 - 19
✸	19 - 21
✸❥💕	21 - 23
€	23 - 00

䷳ 52-Stopping: Make peace with your core and do not get disturbed by emotions.

09:30 EOT 1:00:00 CEST/EDT	Year *Metal* Month *Earth*	壬寅 Water Tiger Year 己酉 Earth Rooster Month 壬寅 Autumn Equinox

October

2022	WEEK 40	Water Tiger Year 9. Lunar Month 8. - 10. Day

3 MO

己丑 Earth Ox — *Fire* — 00:15 ☽ ♑

Roof — Determination — 5 - 4 - 5

00 - 01
01 - 03
03 - 05
05 - 07
07 - 09
09 - 11
11 - 13
13 - 15
15 - 17
17 - 19
19 - 21
21 - 23
23 - 00

15-Modesty: Be modest but not humble or self-deprecating. Engage in common cause.

4 TU

庚寅 Metal Tiger — *Wood* — 10:24 ♒

Room — Rigidity — 5 - 4 - 4

★★★

00 - 01
01 - 03
03 - 05
05 - 07
07 - 09
09 - 11
11 - 13
13 - 15
15 - 17
17 - 19
19 - 21
21 - 23
23 - 00

12-Adversity: Keep your balance and listen to your heart. Savor everyday commodities.

5 WE

辛卯 Metal Rabbit — *Wood* — ♒

Wall — Destruction — 5 - 4 - 3

00 - 01
01 - 03
03 - 05
05 - 07
07 - 09
09 - 11
11 - 13
13 - 15
15 - 17
17 - 19
19 - 21
21 - 23
23 - 00

45-Gathering: Personal sacrifices foster your personal up growth.

10:48 EOT 1:00:00 CEST/EDT	Year *Metal* Month *Earth*	壬寅 Water Tiger Year 己酉 Earth Rooster Month 壬寅 Autumn Equinox

2022	**WEEK 40**	Water Tiger Year 9. Lunar Month 11. - 14. Day

6TH

壬辰 Water Dragon — *Water* — 12:53 ♓
Astride — Danger — 5 - 4 - 2

★★★ ♥ € ❦ ✹ ∅ ✈̸

♥	00 - 01
₠❦✸	01 - 03
✹✈	03 - 05
❥❦	05 - 07
∅❥	07 - 09
✈̸₠⏻✸	09 - 11
✹	11 - 13
∅❥❦	13 - 15
€♥	15 - 17
♥	17 - 19
⚡	19 - 21
€	21 - 23
♥	23 - 00

䷢ 35-Promoting: Be upright, noble and generous. The lust for life evolves from good deeds.

7FR

癸巳 Water Snake — *Water* — ♓
Rope — Completion — 5 - 4 - 1

★ ♥ € ⏻ ✈

✹€	00 - 01
✹♥	01 - 03
✈̸∅₠❥❦	03 - 05
₠❦⏻✸	05 - 07
∅✸❦	07 - 09
	09 - 11
✹❦	11 - 13
✹	13 - 15
∅❦	15 - 17
	17 - 19
€	19 - 21
✹✈⚡	21 - 23
✹€	23 - 00

䷏ 16-Satisfying: Pass your enthusiasm to others. Together you will succeed faster.

8SA

甲午 Wood Horse — *Metal* — 15:56 ♈
Stomach — Harvest / Completion — 5 - 4/3 - 9

★ ❦ ♥ € ⏻ ✈̸ — until 07:23
★★ ❦ ♥ € ⏻ ✈ — from 07:23
07:23 Cold Dew

❦€⚡	00 - 01
❥❦✸	01 - 03
€♥❦	03 - 05
❦	05 - 07
✹	07 - 09
₠✹❦	09 - 11
∅✹❥	11 - 13
✸♥	13 - 15
✹✈	15 - 17
	17 - 19
♥	19 - 21
✈̸₠❥	21 - 23
❦€⚡	23 - 00

䷓ 20-Observing: Take the time to take personal stock as a basis for your spiritual growth.

9SU

乙未 Wood Goat — *Metal* — 20:54 ○ — ♈
Pleiades — Harvest — 5 - 3 - 8

✩✩ € ✈̸

❥❦⏻✸	00 - 01
∅❥⚡	01 - 03
€	03 - 05
€♥	05 - 07
✹❦	07 - 09
✹✈	09 - 11
✹♥	11 - 13
₠	13 - 15
✈̸₠⏻✸	15 - 17
∅❦	17 - 19
∅❥	19 - 21
♥	21 - 23
❥❦⏻✸	23 - 00

䷇ 8-Alliance: Do not hesitate to act jointly.

11:43 EOT 1:00:00 CEST/EDT	Year *Metal* Month *Earth*	壬寅 Water Tiger Year 己酉 Earth Rooster Month 壬寅 Water Tiger Year 壬寅 Metal Dog Month Oct 08 07:23

2022	WEEK 41	Water Tiger Year 9. Lunar Month 15. - 17. Day

10 MO

丙申 Fire Monkey — *Fire* — 20:56 ♉

Net — Opening — 5 - 3 - 7

00 - 01
01 - 03
03 - 05
05 - 07
07 - 09
09 - 11
11 - 13
13 - 15
15 - 17
17 - 19
19 - 21
21 - 23
23 - 00

23-Stripping: Dark clouds are rising. Retreat and bethink yourself.

11 TU

丁酉 Fire Rooster — *Fire* — ♉

Beak — Closing — 5 - 3 - 6

00 - 01
01 - 03
03 - 05
05 - 07
07 - 09
09 - 11
11 - 13
13 - 15
15 - 17
17 - 19
19 - 21
21 - 23
23 - 00

24-Returning: Something re-enters your life. Clarify your ambitions to get a good start.

12 WE

戊戌 Earth Dog — *Wood* — ♉

Orion — Establishment — 5 - 3 - 5

00 - 01
01 - 03
03 - 05
05 - 07
07 - 09
09 - 11
11 - 13
13 - 15
15 - 17
17 - 19
19 - 21
21 - 23
23 - 00

27-Jaws: Take care of your corporal and mental nourishment.

12:52 EOT 1:00:00 CEST/EDT	Year *Metal* Month *Metal*	壬寅 Water Tiger Year 庚戌 Metal Dog Month 壬寅 Cold Dew

2022	**WEEK 41**	Water Tiger Year 9. Lunar Month 18. - 21. Day

⏻✹❦ 00 - 01 01 - 03 ✹♥ 03 - 05 €̸♥ 05 - 07 ✸ 07 - 09 ∅✸✈ϟ 09 - 11 € 11 - 13 ♥ 13 - 15 ✈̸€̸❥❦⏻ 15 - 17 ✸❥❦ 17 - 19 ∅€❦ 19 - 21 ∅❥ 21 - 23 ⏻✹ 23 - 00	**13TH** ★★	己亥 Earth Pig *Wood* 05:00 ♊ Well Removal 5 - 3 - 4 ❦∅✈̸ ☳☷ 3-Accumulating: The start is difficult. Be patient and accept help. You will be successful.
€✹ 00 - 01 ⏻✹♥ 01 - 03 ✈ 03 - 05 ∅❥ 05 - 07 ✸♥ 07 - 09 ✈̸€̸✸ 09 - 11 ❦ϟ 11 - 13 ❥❦ 13 - 15 ✸€♥ 15 - 17 17 - 19 ❦ 19 - 21 ❥ 21 - 23 €✹ 23 - 00	**14FR** ✫✫	庚子 Metal Rat *Earth* ♊ Ghosts Fulfillment 5 - 3 - 3 ♥ € ⏻ ✈ ❦ 42-Increasing: Use your abilities for common welfare. Learn from mistakes.
♥ 00 - 01 ❥✹ 01 - 03 ✈̸⏻✹ 03 - 05 ❦ 05 - 07 ∅✸❦ 07 - 09 ♥ 09 - 11 ❥❦⏻✹ 11 - 13 ∅€̸✸❥ϟ 13 - 15 ❦ 15 - 17 ∅€♥ 17 - 19 ∅❥ 19 - 21 ✈ 21 - 23 ♥ 23 - 00	**15SA** ✫✫	辛丑 Metal Ox *Earth* 16:08 ♋ Willow Balance 5 - 3 - 2 ❦ € ❥∅ 51-Startling: A change is imminent. Keep your calmness and humor, everything will turn to good account.
❦ 00 - 01 ∅✹ 01 - 03 03 - 05 ❥⏻ 05 - 07 ✸€ 07 - 09 ❥❦ 09 - 11 ✸♥❦ 11 - 13 ✹❦ 13 - 15 ∅❥✈ϟ 15 - 17 €̸ 17 - 19 ♥ 19 - 21 ✈̸∅❦♥ 21 - 23 ❦ 23 - 00	**16SU** ✫✫	壬寅 Water Tiger *Metal* ♋ Star Determination 5 - 3 - 1 ❦ ✸ 21-Gnawing And Chewing: Conquer difficulties with discipline and justice.
13:38 EOT 1:00:00 CEST/EDT	Year *Metal* Month *Metal*	壬寅 Water Tiger Year 庚戌 Metal Dog Month 壬寅 Cold Dew

October

2022	**WEEK 42**	Water Tiger Year 9. Lunar Month 22. - 24. Day

17 MO

癸卯 Water Rabbit — *Metal* — 17:16 ☾ ♋

Bow — Rigidity — 5 - 3 - 9

★★ ♥ ♥✸✈

∅✸♥€	00 - 01
∅✸	01 - 03
	03 - 05
⏻✸	05 - 07
♥	07 - 09
♥✈⏻	09 - 11
€	11 - 13
♥	13 - 15
✈€	15 - 17
♥⚡	17 - 19
∅♥	19 - 21
€✸♥	21 - 23
∅✸♥€	23 - 00

17-Following: Learn everything from the scratch and accept advice. This is the basis of authority and recognition.

18 TU

甲辰 Wood Dragon — *Fire* — 04:47 ♌

Wings — Destruction — 5 - 3 - 8

★★⚡ € ♥✸

♥	00 - 01
€♥⏻✸	01 - 03
✸✈€♥	03 - 05
∅✸♥♥	05 - 07
∅♥	07 - 09
✈€♥	09 - 11
✸♥	11 - 13
♥✸	13 - 15
✸€♥	15 - 17
♥	17 - 19
⚡	19 - 21
	21 - 23
♥	23 - 00

25-Without Wrongdoing: Follow your intuition without calculating intention.

19 WE

乙巳 Wood Snake — *Fire* — ♌

Carriage — Danger — 5 - 3 - 7

★★★ ✸✈

⏻✸	00 - 01
♥	01 - 03
✈∅€✸♥♥	03 - 05
✸♥	05 - 07
∅♥	07 - 09
∅	09 - 11
✸	11 - 13
✸	13 - 15
♥✸	15 - 17
	17 - 19
€♥	19 - 21
✈⚡	21 - 23
⏻✸	23 - 00

36-Brightness Wounded: Hide your light under a bushel and persecute your aim.

14:33 EOT 1:00:00 CEST/EDT	Year *Metal* Month *Metal*	壬寅 Water Tiger Year 庚戌 Metal Dog Month 壬寅 Cold Dew

2022	WEEK 42	Water Tiger Year 9. Lunar Month 25. - 28. Day

20TH

丙午 Fire Horse — *Water* — 16:35 ♍

Horn — Completion — 5 - 3 - 6

★★★ ♥♥ ♥ ✸ € ⏻ ✈

♥€✸ϟ	00 - 01
∅♥♥	01 - 03
✸♥	03 - 05
✸	05 - 07
✸	07 - 09
✸	09 - 11
∅♥	11 - 13
∅♥	13 - 15
✈♥	15 - 17
⏻✸	17 - 19
♥	19 - 21
✈€♥⏻✸	21 - 23
♥€✸ϟ	23 - 00

䷕ 22-Adorning: Design everything functional and beautiful because beauty fosters function.

21FR

丁未 Fire Goat — *Water* — ♍

Neck — Harvest — 5 - 3 - 5

☆☆ € ✈

♥♥	00 - 01
∅♥ϟ	01 - 03
✸€♥	03 - 05
✸♥	05 - 07
	07 - 09
✈	09 - 11
€♥♥	11 - 13
€✸	13 - 15
✈€	15 - 17
♥✸	17 - 19
∅♥♥	19 - 21
⏻✸♥	21 - 23
♥	23 - 00

䷾ 63-Already Accomplished: An end is achieved. Finish accurately and prepare for the next begin.

22SA

戊申 Earth Monkey — *Earth* — ♍

Base — Opening — 5 - 3 - 4

★ϟ ♥♥ ♥ € ✈

✸♥	00 - 01
⏻♥	01 - 03
∅✸♥✈ϟ	03 - 05
♥	05 - 07
€♥♥	07 - 09
✈∅♥	09 - 11
♥	11 - 13
✸	13 - 15
✸	15 - 17
€	17 - 19
✸	19 - 21
∅✸♥	21 - 23
✸♥	23 - 00

䷤ 37-Family: Be reliable and consolidate the output as a solid platform for further developments.

23SU

己酉 Earth Rooster — *Earth* — 01:37 ♎

House — Closing — 5 - 3 - 3

☆☆ ⏻ ♥♥ ♥ ✸

10:36 Descent of Frost

⏻✸	00 - 01
∅♥	01 - 03
✈€♥	03 - 05
✸♥ϟ	05 - 07
∅♥	07 - 09
	09 - 11
€	11 - 13
	13 - 15
⏻	15 - 17
∅✸♥	17 - 19
♥	19 - 21
€✈	21 - 23
♥⏻✸	23 - 00

䷶ 55-Overshadowing: Use your wealth with wisdom for your ambitions.

15:07 EOT 1:00:00 CEST/EDT	Year *Metal* Month *Metal*	壬寅 Water Tiger Year 庚戌 Metal Dog Month 壬寅 Descent of Frost Oct 23 10:36

October

2022	**WEEK 43**	Water Tiger Year 9. Lunar Month 29. Day Water Tiger Year 10. Lunar Month 1. - 2. Day

24 MO

庚戌 Metal Dog — *Metal* — ♎
Heart — Establishment — 5 - 3 - 2

☆☆ ♥ ⏻ ✈

♥	00 - 01
€♥✸	01 - 03
✸♥	03 - 05
∅✸♥	05 - 07
ϟ	07 - 09
	09 - 11
♥	11 - 13
♥♥	13 - 15
✸✈€	15 - 17
♥	17 - 19
✸♥	19 - 21
✱€	21 - 23
♥	23 - 00

☲ 30-Brightness: Light your inner fire. Enlighten dark corners and unsettled affairs.

25 TU

辛亥 Metal Pig — *Metal* — 10:48 ● 07:27 ♏
Tail — Removal — 5 - 3 - 1

☆☆ ♥ ∅ ✱

	00 - 01
	01 - 03
♥⏻♥	03 - 05
€✸♥	05 - 07
✸	07 - 09
∅✈ϟ	09 - 11
⏻✸	11 - 13
✸♥	13 - 15
✱€♥	15 - 17
♥♥€	17 - 19
∅€	19 - 21
∅♥	21 - 23
	23 - 00

☱ 49-Reforming: It is a convenient time for changes. Trust in your competence be persistent.

26 WE

壬子 Water Rat — *Wood* — ♏
Basket — Fulfillment — 5 - 3 - 9

☆☆ ♥ € ✈ ♥

€✸	00 - 01
✸♥	01 - 03
✸✈	03 - 05
♥	05 - 07
♥	07 - 09
✱€⏻✸	09 - 11
✸ϟ	11 - 13
∅♥✸	13 - 15
♥	15 - 17
♥	17 - 19
	19 - 21
♥€	21 - 23
€✸	23 - 00

☷ 19-Arriving: Seize the opportunity. Invest in your future.

15:45 EOT 1:00:00 CEST/EDT	Year *Metal* Month *Metal*	壬寅 Water Tiger Year 庚戌 Metal Dog Month 壬寅 Descent of Frost

2022	WEEK 43	Water Tiger Year 10. Lunar Month 3. - 6. Day

27TH

癸丑 Water Ox — *Wood* — 10:54 ♐
Dipper — Balance — 5 - 3 - 8

☆☆ ♥ € ♥ ∅

✸€♥	00 - 01
♥	01 - 03
✶✸	03 - 05
♥⏻	05 - 07
∅✸	07 - 09
⏻♥	09 - 11
♥	11 - 13
∅€♥⚡	13 - 15
	15 - 17
∅♥	17 - 19
∅♥	19 - 21
✸✈	21 - 23
✸€♥	23 - 00

☶ 41-Decreasing: Affiliate honesty with self-restraint. Small things provoke big ones.

28FR

甲寅 Wood Tiger — *Water* — ♐
Ox — Determination — 5 - 3 - 7

☆☆ ♥ ✸

✸♥	00 - 01
	01 - 03
€✸♥	03 - 05
♥	05 - 07
€	07 - 09
∅♥	09 - 11
✸♥	11 - 13
⏻✸	13 - 15
∅✸♥✈⚡	15 - 17
€	17 - 19
♥	19 - 21
✶∅€♥♥	21 - 23
✸♥	23 - 00

☵ 60-Regulating: Identify your limitations. Extend suffocating ones, establish wise ones.

29SA

乙卯 Wood Rabbit — *Water* — 13:17 ♑
Maiden — Rigidity — 5 - 3 - 6

☆☆ ♥ ✸✶

♥	00 - 01
∅✸	01 - 03
	03 - 05
€✸	05 - 07
♥	07 - 09
✸♥✈	09 - 11
✸♥€	11 - 13
✸♥	13 - 15
✶€⏻✸	15 - 17
♥⚡	17 - 19
∅♥♥	19 - 21
€♥	21 - 23
♥	23 - 00

☴ 61-Mutually Trusting: Have an open mind and search for the true core. This arises understanding, adjacency and continuance.

30SU

丙辰 Fire Dragon — *Earth* — ♑
Void — Destruction — 5 - 3 - 5

★⚡ € ⏻ ♥
03:00A CEST Clock changed to 02:00B CET

♥	00 - 01
€✸♥	01 - 03
✈	03 - 05
∅♥	05 - 07
∅✸♥	07 - 09
✶✸	09 - 11
♥	11 - 13
∅♥	13 - 15
€♥♥	15 - 17
⏻✸♥	17 - 19
⚡	19 - 21
⏻✸	21 - 23
♥	23 - 00

☳ 54-The Libidinal Addiction: Be true to your emotions and addiction but with retention.

16:05 EOT 1:00:00 CEST/EDT	Year *Metal* Month *Metal*	壬寅 Water Tiger Year 庚戌 Metal Dog Month 壬寅 Descent of Frost

October

October

2022	WEEK 44	Water Tiger Year 10. Lunar Month 7. - 9. Day

31 MO

丁巳 Fire Snake — *Earth* — 15:42 ♒

Roof — Danger — 5 - 3 - 4

★ ✸ ✗

Halloween

✸	00 - 01
✸♥	01 - 03
✗ø€✸♥	03 - 05
€✸♥	05 - 07
ø	07 - 09
ø✸	09 - 11
€♥	11 - 13
	13 - 15
ø♥	15 - 17
⏻✸	17 - 19
€	19 - 21
✈⏻✸⚡	21 - 23
✸♥	23 - 00

☰ 38-Misunderstanding: Remain true to yourself. Develop individual differences to constructive connections.

1 TU

戊午 Earth Horse — *Fire* — 06:38 ☽ ♒

Room — Completion — 5 - 3 - 3

★★ ♥ ♥ ✸ € ⏻ ✈

✸♥€⚡	00 - 01
♥	01 - 03
♥	03 - 05
♥✸	05 - 07
♥	07 - 09
	09 - 11
ø♥	11 - 13
✸♥	13 - 15
✈	15 - 17
	17 - 19
✸♥	19 - 21
✗€✸♥♥	21 - 23
✸♥€⚡	23 - 00

☰ 58-Pleasing: With an inner smile about yourself and the world you will win the hearts of other people and free your own.

2 WE

己未 Earth Goat — *Fire* — 18:52 ♓

Wall — Harvest — 5 - 3 - 2

★ € ✗

♥⏻	00 - 01
ø✸♥⚡	01 - 03
€✸♥	03 - 05
♥	05 - 07
	07 - 09
✈	09 - 11
€♥	11 - 13
€✸	13 - 15
✗€⏻	15 - 17
ø✸♥	17 - 19
ø♥	19 - 21
♥	21 - 23
♥♥⏻	23 - 00

☰ 10-Treading: Show self-confidence and inner strength together with sereneness.

16:23 EOT 1:00:00 EDT	Year *Metal* Month *Metal*	壬寅 Water Tiger Year 庚戌 Metal Dog Month 壬寅 Descent of Frost

2022	**WEEK 44**	Water Tiger Year 10. Lunar Month 10. - 13. Day

November

3TH

庚申 Metal Monkey — *Wood* — ♓
Astride — Opening — 5 - 3 - 1

00 - 01
01 - 03
03 - 05
05 - 07
07 - 09
09 - 11
11 - 13
13 - 15
15 - 17
17 - 19
19 - 21
21 - 23
23 - 00

11-Prominence: Work together and complement one another. Everyone will profit.

4FR

辛酉 Metal Rooster — *Wood* — 23:11 ♈
Rope — Closing — 5 - 3 - 9

00 - 01
01 - 03
03 - 05
05 - 07
07 - 09
09 - 11
11 - 13
13 - 15
15 - 17
17 - 19
19 - 21
21 - 23
23 - 00

26-Great Gains: Focus your strength. Go out and utilize your capabilities profitably.

5SA

壬戌 Water Dog — *Water* — ♈
Stomach — Establishment — 5 - 3 - 8

00 - 01
01 - 03
03 - 05
05 - 07
07 - 09
09 - 11
11 - 13
13 - 15
15 - 17
17 - 19
19 - 21
21 - 23
23 - 00

5-Waiting: Be patient and pursue your goal, step by step.

6SU

癸亥 Water Pig — *Water* — ♈
Pleiades — Removal — 5 - 3 - 7

02:00A EDT Clock changed to 01:00B EST

00 - 01
01 - 03
03 - 05
05 - 07
07 - 09
09 - 11
11 - 13
13 - 15
15 - 17
17 - 19
19 - 21
21 - 23
23 - 00

9-Small Savings: Go for your ambition with small steps instead of great leaps.

16:27 EOT 1:00:00 EDT	Year *Metal* Month *Metal*	壬寅 Water Tiger Year 庚戌 Metal Dog Month 壬寅 Descent of Frost

2022	**WEEK 45**	Water Tiger Year 10. Lunar Month 14. - 16. Day

7 MO

甲子 Wood Rat — *Metal* — 05:11 ♉
Net — Fulfillment / Removal — 5 - 3/2 - 6

★★ ♥ € ✈ ⚘ ✸ — until 10:46
★★ ✹ ⚘ ⚡ — from 10:46

10:46 Coming of Winter

€ ✹	00 - 01
⏻ ✹ ♥	01 - 03
✈ € ⚘	03 - 05
⌀ ♥	05 - 07
♥	07 - 09
⚡ € ⚘	09 - 11
✸ ⚘ ϟ	11 - 13
♥ ⚘ ✹	13 - 15
✸ ♥	15 - 17
⚘	17 - 19
✸	19 - 21
✸ ♥	21 - 23
€ ✹	23 - 00

䷡ 34-Great Strength: Check your handling of power. Grandeur and justice belong together.

8 TU

乙丑 Wood Ox — *Metal* — 11:02 ○ ♉
Beak — Fulfillment — 5 - 2 - 5

☆☆ ♥ € ✈

⏻ ✹ ♥	00 - 01
♥ ✹	01 - 03
⚡	03 - 05
⚘ €	05 - 07
⌀	07 - 09
✸ ♥	09 - 11
✸ ♥ ⚘	11 - 13
⌀ € ✸ ♥ ϟ	13 - 15
⏻ ✹	15 - 17
⌀ ♥	17 - 19
⌀ ✸ ♥ ⚘	19 - 21
✸ ✈	21 - 23
⏻ ✹ ♥	23 - 00

䷍ 14-Great Reward: Use your capabilities and assets for common weal.

9 WE

丙寅 Fire Tiger — *Fire* — 13:29 ♊
Orion — Balance — 5 - 2 - 4

☆☆ ♥ ✸ ⌀

⚘ ✹	00 - 01
⌀	01 - 03
✹	03 - 05
♥ ⚘	05 - 07
✸ €	07 - 09
⌀ ✸ ♥ ⚘ €	09 - 11
♥	11 - 13
	13 - 15
⌀ ♥ ✈ ⚘ ϟ	15 - 17
€ ⏻ ✹	17 - 19
✸ ♥	19 - 21
⚡ € ⚘ ♥	21 - 23
⚘ ✹	23 - 00

䷪ 43-Severing: Stand up frankly for your own truth. Be determined but not offending.

16:21 EOT 0:00:00 CET/EST	Year *Metal* Month *Metal*	壬寅 Water Tiger Year 庚戌 Metal Dog Month 壬寅 Water Tiger Year 壬寅 Metal Pig Month — Nov 07 10:46

10TH

丁卯 Fire Rabbit   *Fire*   Ⅱ

Well   Determination   5 - 2 - 3

★★   ♥ ✳

∅♥	00 - 01
∅	01 - 03
✳♥	03 - 05
	05 - 07
⚥♥	07 - 09
⚥⚵	09 - 11
€	11 - 13
♥	13 - 15
⚵€	15 - 17
♥☉✳⚡	17 - 19
∅✳♥	19 - 21
€☉♥	21 - 23
∅⚥♥	23 - 00

44-Meeting: Examine a seductive offer with minuteness and hold off.

11FR

戊辰 Earth Dragon   *Wood*   Ⅱ

Ghosts   Rigidity   5 - 2 - 2

⚵⚵   ♥ ✳ ⚵

✳♥	00 - 01
€☉	01 - 03
⚵	03 - 05
∅⚥♥✳	05 - 07
∅⚥♥	07 - 09
⚵	09 - 11
♥	11 - 13
⚥✳	13 - 15
€♥	15 - 17
♥	17 - 19
✳⚡	19 - 21
✳♥	21 - 23
✳♥	23 - 00

28-Great Test: Do not blow your plans out of proportions. Be gentle and mind your balance.

12SA

己巳 Earth Snake   *Wood*   00:12 ♋

Willow   Destruction   5 - 2 - 1

⚵⚵⚡   ⚵ ♥ ♥ ✳

☉●♥	00 - 01
♥	01 - 03
⚵∅€♥●	03 - 05
€♥	05 - 07
∅	07 - 09
∅●	09 - 11
€	11 - 13
	13 - 15
♥	15 - 17
⚵	17 - 19
✳€♥	19 - 21
✳⚵⚡	21 - 23
☉●	23 - 00

50-The Caldron: Sort out material and spiritual ballast and create free space for new ideas.

13SU

庚午 Metal Horse   *Earth*   ♋

Star   Danger   5 - 2 - 9

★★   ♥ ✳ ⚵

♥€⚡	00 - 01
⚵♥●	01 - 03
♥	03 - 05
♥	05 - 07
	07 - 09
€	09 - 11
∅♥	11 - 13
♥	13 - 15
✳⚵€	15 - 17
♥	17 - 19
✳♥♥	19 - 21
⚵€♥	21 - 23
♥€⚡	23 - 00

32-Constancy: Take up a solid position without freezing.

16:08 EOT	Year *Metal*	壬寅 Water Tiger Year 辛亥 Metal Pig Month
0:00:00 CET/EST	Month *Metal*	壬寅 Coming of Winter

November

2022	**WEEK 46**	Water Tiger Year 10. Lunar Month 21. - 23. Day

14 MO

辛未 Metal Goat — *Earth* — 12:35 ♌
Bow — Completion — 5 - 2 - 8

★★ ♥♥ ♥ ✹ € ⏻ ✈

♥♥♥	00 - 01
⌀♥⚡	01 - 03
⏻€✹	03 - 05
♥	05 - 07
✹	07 - 09
✈	09 - 11
⏻✹♥	11 - 13
€	13 - 15
✈€♥♥	15 - 17
⌀♥♥€	17 - 19
⌀✹♥♥♥	19 - 21
✹♥	21 - 23
♥♥♥	23 - 00

57-Penetrating: Get your goals clear and implement them, gentle but consequent.

15 TU

壬申 Water Monkey — *Metal* — ♌
Wings — Harvest — 5 - 2 - 7

✗★⚡ ⏻

♥	00 - 01
✹	01 - 03
⌀✹♥✈⚡	03 - 05
♥⏻	05 - 07
€♥	07 - 09
✈€♥♥✹	09 - 11
✹	11 - 13
⌀✹♥♥	13 - 15
✹	15 - 17
€	17 - 19
✹	19 - 21
⌀✹♥♥♥€	21 - 23
♥	23 - 00

48-The Well: Develop your potentials and take good care of yourself.

16 WE

癸酉 Water Rooster — *Metal* — 13:29 ☾ ♌
Carriage — Opening — 5 - 2 - 6

★★ ♥ € ✈

✹♥♥€	00 - 01
⌀✹♥	01 - 03
✈€	03 - 05
♥♥⏻✹⚡	05 - 07
⌀✹♥♥♥	07 - 09
⏻	09 - 11
€♥♥	11 - 13
	13 - 15
	15 - 17
⌀♥	17 - 19
♥♥♥	19 - 21
€✹✈	21 - 23
✹♥♥€	23 - 00

18-Decaying: Do not be too good for humble work. Clear backlog.

15:39 EOT 0:00:00 CET/EST	Year *Metal* Month *Metal*	壬寅 Water Tiger Year 辛亥 Metal Pig Month 壬寅 Coming of Winter

2022	WEEK 46	Water Tiger Year 10. Lunar Month 24. - 27. Day

17TH

甲戌 Wood Dog — *Fire* — 00:55 ♍

Horn — Closing — 5 - 2 - 5

★★

❦ 00 - 01
€♥✹ 01 - 03
€♥❦ 03 - 05
∅♥ 05 - 07
⚡ 07 - 09
❦ 09 - 11
✹♥ 11 - 13
♥❦✹ 13 - 15
✹✈€ 15 - 17
♥❦ 17 - 19
✹ 19 - 21
✗€ 21 - 23
❦ 23 - 00

䷭ 46-Rising: Rely on your intuition. Put your plans into action - now.

18FR

乙亥 Wood Pig — *Fire* — ♍

Neck — Establishment — 5 - 2 - 4

★ ❦

⏻✹ 00 - 01
01 - 03
❦♥ 03 - 05
♥ 05 - 07
❦ 07 - 09
∅✹✈⚡ 09 - 11
✹ 11 - 13
✹♥ 13 - 15
✗€♥❦⏻ 15 - 17
✹♥❦ 17 - 19
∅€❦ 19 - 21
∅♥ 21 - 23
⏻✹ 23 - 00

䷅ 6-Litigating:
Be honest but not stubborn or impolite. Solve a conflict with empathy and compromising.

19SA

丙子 Fire Rat — *Water* — 10:58 ♎

Base — Removal — 5 - 2 - 3

✗✗ ∅✗

€✹ 00 - 01
♥ 01 - 03
✈ 03 - 05
∅♥❦ 05 - 07
✹♥ 07 - 09
✗✹ 09 - 11
❦⚡ 11 - 13
∅♥❦ 13 - 15
✹♥❦ 15 - 17
❦⏻ 17 - 19
19 - 21
♥⏻✹ 21 - 23
€✹ 23 - 00

䷮ 47-Confining: Benefit from your problems for your progress but do not talk about it.

20SU

丁丑 Fire Ox — *Water* — ♎

House — Fulfillment — 5 - 2 - 2

✗✗ ❦♥€✈ ∅

♥ 00 - 01
♥✹ 01 - 03
✗✹❦ 03 - 05
✹❦ 05 - 07
∅❦ 07 - 09
♥ 09 - 11
♥€ 11 - 13
∅€♥⚡ 13 - 15
✹ 15 - 17
♥ 17 - 19
∅♥ 19 - 21
✈⏻✹ 21 - 23
♥❦ 23 - 00

䷿ 64-Not Yet Accomplished: Specify precisely what you want to start but finish it definitely.

15:08 EOT 0:00:00 CET/EST	Year *Metal* Month *Metal*	壬寅 Water Tiger Year 辛亥 Metal Pig Month 壬寅 Coming of Winter

2022	**WEEK 47**	Water Tiger Year 10. Lunar Month 28. - 30. Day

21 MO

戊寅 Earth Tiger — *Earth* — 17:22 ♏
Heart — Balance — 5 - 2 - 1

✸♥ ♥ ✸ ∅

✸♥	00 - 01
♥	01 - 03
✸	03 - 05
♥✸	05 - 07
€♥	07 - 09
∅♥♥€	09 - 11
♥	11 - 13
⏻✸	13 - 15
∅✸♥✈⚡	15 - 17
€✸	17 - 19
✸♥	19 - 21
✈∅€✸♥	21 - 23
✸♥	23 - 00

40-Separating: Disengage yourself from dead weight and return to your roots. Complete necessary objectives immediately.

22 TU

己卯 Earth Rabbit — *Earth* — ♏
Tail — Determination — 5 - 2 - 9

★★★ ♥ ✸
08:21 Slight Snow

♥✸♥	00 - 01
∅	01 - 03
✸♥	03 - 05
✸	05 - 07
♥♥	07 - 09
♥✈	09 - 11
♥€	11 - 13
♥	13 - 15
✈€⏻	15 - 17
✸♥⚡	17 - 19
∅♥♥	19 - 21
€♥	21 - 23
♥✸	23 - 00

59-Dispersing: Break deadlocked structures with changes and shared joy.

23 WE

庚辰 Metal Dragon — *Metal* — 22:57 ● 20:20 ♐
Basket — Rigidity — 5 - 2 - 8

✸✸ ♥✸✈

♥	00 - 01
€♥⏻✸	01 - 03
✈	03 - 05
∅♥♥	05 - 07
∅♥	07 - 09
✈€	09 - 11
♥	11 - 13
♥	13 - 15
✸€♥	15 - 17
✸♥♥	17 - 19
♥⚡	19 - 21
	21 - 23
♥	23 - 00

29-Cavern: Be truly and sincere to yourself. Overcome obstacles peacefully.

14:15 EOT 0:00:00 CET/EST	Year *Metal* Month *Metal*	壬寅 Water Tiger Year 辛亥 Metal Pig Month 壬寅 Slight Snow Nov 22 08:21

2022	WEEK 47	Water Tiger Year 11. Lunar Month 1. - 4. Day

November

24TH

辛巳 Metal Snake — *Metal* — ♐
Dipper — Destruction — 5 - 2 - 7

	00 - 01
♥	01 - 03
	03 - 05
€	05 - 07
	07 - 09
	09 - 11
⏻	11 - 13
	13 - 15
	15 - 17
€	17 - 19
€	19 - 21
✈ϟ	21 - 23
	23 - 00

4-Ignorance: Be enthusiastic and open minded but rely on your experience.

25FR

壬午 Water Horse — *Wood* — 21:19 ♑
Ox — Danger — 5 - 2 - 6

★★

€ϟ	00 - 01
♥	01 - 03
♥	03 - 05
⏻	05 - 07
	07 - 09
⏻	09 - 11
♥	11 - 13
♥	13 - 15
✈	15 - 17
	17 - 19
♥	19 - 21
	21 - 23
€ϟ	23 - 00

33-Retiring: A retreat in the right moment saves your dignity. Be insistent.

26SA

癸未 Water Goat — *Wood* — ♑
Maiden — Completion — 5 - 2 - 5

★★★ ♥ € ⏻ ✈

€	00 - 01
ϟ	01 - 03
€	03 - 05
⏻ ♥	05 - 07
	07 - 09
✈⏻	09 - 11
♥	11 - 13
	13 - 15
	15 - 17
	17 - 19
	19 - 21
♥	21 - 23
€	23 - 00

31-Influencing:
Reconcile your ambitions and your needs. Use the natural power of attraction of all things.

27SU

甲申 Wood Monkey — *Water* — 22:08 ♒
Void — Harvest — 5 - 2 - 4

★★★ϟ ⏻
1. Advent

♥	00 - 01
⏻	01 - 03
✈€ϟ	03 - 05
	05 - 07
€♥	07 - 09
	09 - 11
	11 - 13
	13 - 15
	15 - 17
	17 - 19
	19 - 21
	21 - 23
♥	23 - 00

56-Traveling: Scoop from your inner source, be attentive and start for new shore.

13:27 EOT 0:00:00 CET/EST	Year *Metal* Month *Metal*	壬寅 Water Tiger Year 辛亥 Metal Pig Month 壬寅 Slight Snow

2022	WEEK 48	Water Tiger Year 11. Lunar Month 5. - 7. Day

28 MO

乙酉 Wood Rooster — *Water* — ≈
Roof — Opening — 5 - 2 - 3

★★★ ♥ € ⏻ ✈

♥⏻✸	00 - 01
∅♥	01 - 03
✈€	03 - 05
♥€ϟ	05 - 07
∅♥♥	07 - 09
✸	09 - 11
✸€	11 - 13
✸	13 - 15
⏻✸	15 - 17
∅♥	17 - 19
♥	19 - 21
€✈	21 - 23
♥⏻✸	23 - 00

䷽ 62-Small Testing: Concentrate on the details and complete them with accuracy.

29 TU

丙戌 Fire Dog — *Earth* — ≈
Room — Closing — 5 - 2 - 2

☆☆ ♥ ✸

♥✸	00 - 01
∅€♥	01 - 03
♥	03 - 05
∅♥♥	05 - 07
✸ϟ	07 - 09
✸€	09 - 11
✸♥	11 - 13
∅✸♥♥	13 - 15
✈€♥	15 - 17
♥♥⏻✸	17 - 19
✸	19 - 21
✈€⏻✸	21 - 23
♥✸	23 - 00

䷴ 53-Gradually Progressing: Achieve your plans, patient and with integrity.

30 WE

丁亥 Fire Pig — *Earth* — 14:38 ☽ 00:21 ♓
Wall — Establishment — 5 - 2 - 1

☆☆

	00 - 01
	01 - 03
✸♥	03 - 05
€✸♥	05 - 07
	07 - 09
∅✈ϟ	09 - 11
✸€♥	11 - 13
✸♥	13 - 15
✈€♥♥	15 - 17
♥♥⏻✸	17 - 19
∅€	19 - 21
♥✸	21 - 23
♥	23 - 00

䷦ 39-Obstructing: Do not bash your head against a wall. Retreat, bethink and talk to friends.

12:12 EOT 0:00:00 CET/EST	Year *Metal* Month *Metal*	壬寅 Water Tiger Year 辛亥 Metal Pig Month 壬寅 Slight Snow

2022	WEEK 48	Water Tiger Year 11. Lunar Month 8. - 11. Day

1 TH

戊子 Earth Rat — *Fire* — ♓

Astride — Removal — 5 - 2 - 9

✰✰ ♥ ∅ ✶

€	00 - 01
⏻♥♥	01 - 03
✈	03 - 05
∅♥✸	05 - 07
♥♥	07 - 09
✶	09 - 11
✸♥⚡	11 - 13
♥♥	13 - 15
♥	15 - 17
♥	17 - 19
✸	19 - 21
✸♥♥	21 - 23
€	23 - 00

䷳ 52-Stopping: Make peace with your core and do not get disturbed by emotions.

2 FR

己丑 Earth Ox — *Fire* — 04:49 ♈

Rope — Fulfillment — 5 - 2 - 8

✰✰ ♥ € ✈ ∅

⏻✸♥♥	00 - 01
♥✸	01 - 03
✶✸♥	03 - 05
♥	05 - 07
∅♥	07 - 09
♥	09 - 11
✸♥♥€	11 - 13
∅€✸♥⚡	13 - 15
⏻	15 - 17
∅✸♥	17 - 19
∅♥♥	19 - 21
✈	21 - 23
⏻✸♥	23 - 00

䷎ 15-Modesty: Be modest but not humble or self-deprecating. Engage in common cause.

3 SA

庚寅 Metal Tiger — *Wood* — ♈

Stomach — Balance — 5 - 2 - 7

★★ ♥ ✸∅

♥	00 - 01
✸	01 - 03
✸	03 - 05
♥	05 - 07
€	07 - 09
∅♥♥	09 - 11
♥	11 - 13
⏻	13 - 15
∅✸♥✈€⚡	15 - 17
€♥	17 - 19
♥♥	19 - 21
✶∅€♥♥	21 - 23
♥	23 - 00

䷋ 12-Adversity: Keep your balance and listen to your heart. Savor everyday commodities.

4 SU

辛卯 Metal Rabbit — *Wood* — 11:41 ♉

Pleiades — Determination — 5 - 2 - 6

★★★ ♥ ✸

2. Advent

∅♥	00 - 01
∅	01 - 03
⏻✸	03 - 05
✸	05 - 07
✸♥♥	07 - 09
♥✈	09 - 11
♥⏻€	11 - 13
✸♥	13 - 15
✶€♥	15 - 17
♥€⚡	17 - 19
∅♥	19 - 21
€♥	21 - 23
∅♥	23 - 00

䷬ 45-Gathering: Personal sacrifices foster your personal up growth.

11:09 EOT 0:00:00 CET/EST	Year *Metal* Month *Metal*	壬寅 Water Tiger Year 辛亥 Metal Pig Month 壬寅 Slight Snow

2022	**WEEK 49**	Water Tiger Year 11. Lunar Month 12. - 14. Day

5 MO

壬辰 Water Dragon — *Water* — ♉
Net — Rigidity — 5 - 2 - 5

☆☆ ♥♥ ✸ ✈

♥	00 - 01
€♥✸	01 - 03
✸✈	03 - 05
♥♥	05 - 07
Ø♥	07 - 09
✈€⏻✸	09 - 11
✸	11 - 13
Ø♥♥	13 - 15
€♥	15 - 17
♥	17 - 19
ϟ	19 - 21
€	21 - 23
♥	23 - 00

☲☷ 35-Promoting: Be upright, noble and generous. The lust for life evolves from good deeds.

6 TU

癸巳 Water Snake — *Water* — 20:46 ♊
Beak — Destruction — 5 - 2 - 4

☆☆ϟ ✈ ♥♥ ✸
Saint Nicholas

✸€	00 - 01
✸♥	01 - 03
✈Ø€♥♥	03 - 05
€♥⏻✸	05 - 07
Ø✸♥	07 - 09
	09 - 11
✸♥	11 - 13
✸	13 - 15
Ø♥	15 - 17
	17 - 19
€	19 - 21
✸✈ϟ	21 - 23
✸€	23 - 00

☳☷ 16-Satisfying: Pass your enthusiasm to others. Together you will succeed faster.

7 WE

甲午 Wood Horse — *Metal* — ♊
Orion — Danger / Destruction — 5 - 2/1 - 3

★★★ ⏻ ♥✈ — until 03:47
☆☆ϟ ⏻ ♥♥ ✸ — from 03:47
03:47 Great Snow

♥€ϟ	00 - 01
♥♥✸	01 - 03
€♥♥	03 - 05
♥	05 - 07
✸	07 - 09
€✸♥	09 - 11
Ø✸♥	11 - 13
✸♥	13 - 15
✸✈	15 - 17
	17 - 19
♥	19 - 21
✈€♥	21 - 23
♥€ϟ	23 - 00

☴☷ 20-Observing: Take the time to take personal stock as a basis for your spiritual growth.

09:35 EOT 0:00:00 CET/EST	Year *Metal* Month *Metal*	壬寅 Water Tiger Year 辛亥 Metal Pig Month 壬寅 Water Tiger Year 壬寅 Water Rat Month Dec 07 03:47

2022	WEEK 49	Water Tiger Year	11. Lunar Month	15. - 18. Day

8TH

乙未 Wood Goat — *Metal* — 04:09 ○ — ♊

Well — Danger — 5 - 1 - 2

00 - 01	
01 - 03	
03 - 05	
05 - 07	
07 - 09	
09 - 11	
11 - 13	
13 - 15	
15 - 17	
17 - 19	
19 - 21	
21 - 23	
23 - 00	

8-Alliance: Do not hesitate to act jointly.

9FR

丙申 Fire Monkey — *Fire* — 07:42 ♋

Ghosts — Completion — 5 - 1 - 1

00 - 01	
01 - 03	
03 - 05	
05 - 07	
07 - 09	
09 - 11	
11 - 13	
13 - 15	
15 - 17	
17 - 19	
19 - 21	
21 - 23	
23 - 00	

23-Stripping: Dark clouds are rising. Retreat and bethink yourself.

10SA

丁酉 Fire Rooster — *Fire* — ♋

Willow — Harvest — 5 - 1 - 9

00 - 01	
01 - 03	
03 - 05	
05 - 07	
07 - 09	
09 - 11	
11 - 13	
13 - 15	
15 - 17	
17 - 19	
19 - 21	
21 - 23	
23 - 00	

24-Returning: Something re-enters your life. Clarify your ambitions to get a good start.

11SU

戊戌 Earth Dog — *Wood* — 19:55 ♌

Star — Opening — 5 - 1 - 8

3. Advent

00 - 01	
01 - 03	
03 - 05	
05 - 07	
07 - 09	
09 - 11	
11 - 13	
13 - 15	
15 - 17	
17 - 19	
19 - 21	
21 - 23	
23 - 00	

27-Jaws: Take care of your corporal and mental nourishment.

08:19 EOT 0:00:00 CET/EST	Year *Metal* Month *Wood*	壬寅 Water Tiger Year 壬子 Water Rat Month 壬寅 Great Snow

December

2022	WEEK 50	Water Tiger Year 11. Lunar Month 19. - 21. Day

12 MO

己亥 Earth Pig *Wood* ♌
Bow Closing 5 - 1 - 7

★★★ ⏻ ♥♥ ✹ ⚡

⏻ ✹ ♥	00 - 01
	01 - 03
✹ ♥	03 - 05
€ ♥	05 - 07
✹	07 - 09
∅ ✹ ✈ ϟ	09 - 11
€	11 - 13
♥	13 - 15
⚡ € ♥ ♥ ⏻	15 - 17
✹ ♥ ♥	17 - 19
∅ € ♥	19 - 21
∅ ♥	21 - 23
⏻ ✹	23 - 00

☷ 3-Accumulating: The start is difficult. Be patient and accept help. You will be successful.

13 TU

庚子 Metal Rat *Earth* ♌
Wings Establishment 5 - 1 - 6

∅∅ ♥ ⏻ ✈ ♥ €

€ ✹	00 - 01
⏻ ✹ ♥	01 - 03
✈	03 - 05
∅ ♥	05 - 07
✹ ♥	07 - 09
⚡ € ✹	09 - 11
♥ ϟ	11 - 13
♥ ♥	13 - 15
✹ € ♥	15 - 17
	17 - 19
♥	19 - 21
♥	21 - 23
€ ✹	23 - 00

☷ 42-Increasing: Use your abilities for common welfare. Learn from mistakes.

14 WE

辛丑 Metal Ox *Earth* 08:26 ♍
Carriage Removal 5 - 1 - 5

★★ ♥ ♥ ∅ ⚡

♥	00 - 01
♥ ✹	01 - 03
⚡ ⏻ ✹	03 - 05
♥	05 - 07
∅ ✹ ♥	07 - 09
♥	09 - 11
♥ ♥ ⏻ ✹	11 - 13
∅ € ✹ ♥ ϟ	13 - 15
♥	15 - 17
∅ € ♥	17 - 19
∅ ♥	19 - 21
✈	21 - 23
♥	23 - 00

☷ 51-Startling:
A change is imminent. Keep your calmness and humor, everything will turn to good account.

06:32 EOT 0:00:00 CET/EST	Year *Metal* Month *Wood*	壬寅 Water Tiger Year 壬子 Water Rat Month 壬寅 Great Snow

15TH

壬寅 Water Tiger — *Metal* — ♍

Horn — Fulfillment — 5 - 1 - 4

★★★ ♥ € ⏻ ✈

00 - 01
01 - 03
03 - 05
05 - 07
07 - 09
09 - 11
11 - 13
13 - 15
15 - 17
17 - 19
19 - 21
21 - 23
23 - 00

21-Gnawing And Chewing: Conquer difficulties with discipline and justice.

16FR

癸卯 Water Rabbit — *Metal* — 08:59 ☾ 19:33 ♎

Neck — Balance — 5 - 1 - 3

00 - 01
01 - 03
03 - 05
05 - 07
07 - 09
09 - 11
11 - 13
13 - 15
15 - 17
17 - 19
19 - 21
21 - 23
23 - 00

17-Following: Learn everything from the scratch and accept advice. This is the basis of authority and recognition.

17SA

甲辰 Wood Dragon — *Fire* — ♎

Base — Determination — 5 - 1 - 2

00 - 01
01 - 03
03 - 05
05 - 07
07 - 09
09 - 11
11 - 13
13 - 15
15 - 17
17 - 19
19 - 21
21 - 23
23 - 00

25-Without Wrongdoing: Follow your intuition without calculating intention.

18SU

乙巳 Wood Snake — *Fire* — ♎

House — Rigidity — 5 - 1 - 1

★★★

4. Advent

00 - 01
01 - 03
03 - 05
05 - 07
07 - 09
09 - 11
11 - 13
13 - 15
15 - 17
17 - 19
19 - 21
21 - 23
23 - 00

36-Brightness Wounded: Hide your light under a bushel and persecute your aim.

05:07 EOT 0:00:00 CET/EST	Year *Metal* Month *Wood*	壬寅 Water Tiger Year 壬子 Water Rat Month 壬寅 Great Snow

2022	**WEEK 51**	Water Tiger Year 11. Lunar Month 26. - 28. Day

December

19 MO

丙午 Fire Horse — *Water* — 03:24 ♏
Heart — Destruction — 5 - 1 - 9

00 - 01
01 - 03
03 - 05
05 - 07
07 - 09
09 - 11
11 - 13
13 - 15
15 - 17
17 - 19
19 - 21
21 - 23
23 - 00

22-Adorning: Design everything functional and beautiful because beauty fosters function.

20 TU

丁未 Fire Goat — *Water* — ♏
Tail — Danger — 5 - 1 - 8

★★★

00 - 01
01 - 03
03 - 05
05 - 07
07 - 09
09 - 11
11 - 13
13 - 15
15 - 17
17 - 19
19 - 21
21 - 23
23 - 00

63-Already Accomplished: An end is achieved. Finish accurately and prepare for the next begin.

21 WE

戊申 Earth Monkey — *Earth* — 07:12 ♐
Basket — Completion — 5 - 1 - 7/3

★★★

21:49 Winter Solstice

00 - 01
01 - 03
03 - 05
05 - 07
07 - 09
09 - 11
11 - 13
13 - 15
15 - 17
17 - 19
19 - 21
21 - 23
23 - 00

37-Family: Be reliable and consolidate the output as a solid platform for further developments.

03:11 EOT 0:00:00 CET/EST	Year *Metal* Month *Wood*	壬寅 Water Tiger Year 壬子 Water Rat Month 壬寅 Winter Solstice Dec 21 21:49

2022	WEEK 51	Water Tiger Year 11. Lunar Month 29. Day Water Tiger Year 12. Lunar Month 1. - 3. Day
00 - 01 01 - 03 03 - 05 05 - 07 07 - 09 09 - 11 11 - 13 13 - 15 15 - 17 17 - 19 19 - 21 21 - 23 23 - 00	22TH	己酉 Earth Rooster *Earth* ♐ Dipper Harvest 5 - 1 - 4 55-Overshadowing: Use your wealth with wisdom for your ambitions.
00 - 01 01 - 03 03 - 05 05 - 07 07 - 09 09 - 11 11 - 13 13 - 15 15 - 17 17 - 19 19 - 21 21 - 23 23 - 00	23FR	庚戌 Metal Dog *Metal* 10:17 ● 07:51 ♑ Ox Opening 5 - 1 - 5 30-Brightness: Light your inner fire. Enlighten dark corners and unsettled affairs.
00 - 01 01 - 03 03 - 05 05 - 07 07 - 09 09 - 11 11 - 13 13 - 15 15 - 17 17 - 19 19 - 21 21 - 23 23 - 00	24SA	辛亥 Metal Pig *Metal* ♑ Maiden Closing 5 - 1 - 6 Christmas Eve 49-Reforming: It is a convenient time for changes. Trust in your competence be persistent.
00 - 01 01 - 03 03 - 05 05 - 07 07 - 09 09 - 11 11 - 13 13 - 15 15 - 17 17 - 19 19 - 21 21 - 23 23 - 00	25SU	壬子 Water Rat *Wood* 07:17 ♒ Void Establishment 5 - 1 - 7 Christmas 19-Arriving: Seize the opportunity. Invest in your future.
01:43 EOT 0:00:00 CET/EST	Year *Metal* Month *Wood*	壬寅 Water Tiger Year 壬子 Water Rat Month 壬寅 Winter Solstice

2022	**WEEK 52**	Water Tiger Year 12. Lunar Month 4. - 6. Day

26 MO

癸丑 Water Ox — *Wood* — ♒
Roof — Removal — 5 - 1 - 8

★★ ♥ ❦⌀✗

✸€♥	00 - 01
❦	01 - 03
✗✸	03 - 05
❦⏻	05 - 07
⌀✹	07 - 09
⏻♥	09 - 11
❦	11 - 13
⌀€❦ϟ	13 - 15
	15 - 17
⌀♥	17 - 19
⌀❦	19 - 21
✸✈	21 - 23
✸€♥	23 - 00

☶☱ 41-Decreasing: Affiliate honesty with self-restraint. Small things provoke big ones.

27 TU

甲寅 Wood Tiger — *Water* — 07:41 ♓
Room — Fulfillment — 5 - 1 - 9

★ ♥€⏻✈ ✸

✸❦	00 - 01
	01 - 03
€✹❦	03 - 05
❦	05 - 07
€	07 - 09
⌀❦	09 - 11
✸♥	11 - 13
⏻✹	13 - 15
⌀✸❦✈ϟ	15 - 17
€	17 - 19
♥	19 - 21
✗⌀€❦♥	21 - 23
✸❦	23 - 00

☵☱ 60-Regulating: Identify your limitations. Extend suffocating ones, establish wise ones.

28 WE

乙卯 Wood Rabbit — *Water* — ♓
Wall — Balance — 5 - 1 - 1

★★ ❦ ❦✸⌀

❦	00 - 01
⌀✸	01 - 03
	03 - 05
€✹	05 - 07
❦	07 - 09
✸❦✈	09 - 11
✸❦€	11 - 13
✸♥	13 - 15
✗€⏻✹	15 - 17
❦ϟ	17 - 19
⌀♥❦	19 - 21
€♥	21 - 23
❦	23 - 00

☴☱ 61-Mutually Trusting: Have an open mind and search for the true core. This arises understanding, adjacency and continuance.

-00:15 EOT 0:00:00 CET/EST	Year *Metal* Month *Wood*	壬寅 Water Tiger Year 壬子 Water Rat Month 壬寅 Winter Solstice

2022	**WEEK 52**	Water Tiger Year 12. Lunar Month 7. - 10. Day

29TH

丙辰 Fire Dragon — *Earth* — 10:48 ♈

Astride — Determination — 5 - 1 - 2

☆ ♥ ✱

♥	00 - 01
€✱♥	01 - 03
✢	03 - 05
∅♥	05 - 07
∅✱♥	07 - 09
✢✱	09 - 11
♥	11 - 13
∅♥	13 - 15
€♥♥	15 - 17
⏻✱♥	17 - 19
ϟ	19 - 21
⏻✱	21 - 23
♥	23 - 00

☳ 54-The Libidinal Addiction: Be true to your emotions and addiction but with retention.

30FR

丁巳 Fire Snake — *Earth* — 01:22 ☽ ♈

Rope — Rigidity — 5 - 1 - 3

☆☆ ⏻ €✢

✱	00 - 01
✱♥	01 - 03
✢∅€✱♥	03 - 05
€✱♥	05 - 07
∅	07 - 09
∅✱	09 - 11
€♥	11 - 13
	13 - 15
∅♥	15 - 17
⏻✱	17 - 19
€	19 - 21
✢⏻✱ϟ	21 - 23
✱♥	23 - 00

☲ 38-Misunderstanding:
Remain true to yourself. Develop individual differences to constructive connections.

31SA

戊午 Earth Horse — *Fire* — 17:22 ♉

Stomach — Destruction — 5 - 1 - 4

☆☆ϟ ♥♥✱

New Year's Eve

✱♥€ϟ	00 - 01
♥	01 - 03
♥	03 - 05
♥✱	05 - 07
♥	07 - 09
	09 - 11
∅♥	11 - 13
✱♥	13 - 15
✢	15 - 17
	17 - 19
✱♥	19 - 21
✢€✱♥♥	21 - 23
✱♥€ϟ	23 - 00

☱ 58-Pleasing: With an inner smile about yourself and the world you will win the hearts of other people and free your own.

1SU

己未 Earth Goat — *Fire* — ♉

Pleiades — Danger — 5 - 1 - 5

★★ ♥♥✱∅✢

New Year's Day

♥⏻	00 - 01
∅✱♥ϟ	01 - 03
€✱♥	03 - 05
♥	05 - 07
	07 - 09
✢	09 - 11
€♥	11 - 13
€✱	13 - 15
✢€⏻	15 - 17
∅✱♥	17 - 19
∅♥	19 - 21
♥	21 - 23
♥♥⏻	23 - 00

☰ 10-Treading: Show self-confidence and inner strength together with sereneness.

-01:43 EOT 0:00:00 CET/EST	Year *Metal* Month *Wood*	壬寅 Water Tiger Year 壬子 Water Rat Month 壬寅 Winter Solstice

January

2023	**WEEK 1**	Water Tiger Year 12. Lunar Month 11. - 13. Day

2 MO

庚申 Metal Monkey — *Wood* — ♉
Net — Completion — 5 - 1 - 6

✰ϟ   ♥♥ ✸ € ⏻ ✈

✸♥	00 - 01
⏻	01 - 03
⌀♥✈ϟ	03 - 05
♥	05 - 07
€♥	07 - 09
✈⌀€♥	09 - 11
♥	11 - 13
	13 - 15
€	15 - 17
€♥	17 - 19
♥	19 - 21
⌀♥♥	21 - 23
✸♥	23 - 00

☷☰ 11-Prominence: Work together and complement one another. Everyone will profit.

3 TU

辛酉 Metal Rooster — *Wood* — 02:53 ♊
Beak — Harvest — 5 - 1 - 7

✰✰   ♥ € ⏻ ✈

✸♥	00 - 01
⌀✸♥	01 - 03
✈€⏻✸	03 - 05
♥ϟ	05 - 07
⌀✸♥	07 - 09
	09 - 11
⏻€✸	11 - 13
✸	13 - 15
♥	15 - 17
⌀♥€	17 - 19
♥♥	19 - 21
€✈	21 - 23
✸♥	23 - 00

☶☰ 26-Great Gains: Focus your strength. Go out and utilize your capabilities profitably.

4 WE

壬戌 Water Dog — *Water* — ♊
Orion — Opening — 5 - 1 - 8

✰✰   ♥♥ ✸ ⏻ ✈

✸♥	00 - 01
⌀€♥	01 - 03
✸♥	03 - 05
♥	05 - 07
ϟ	07 - 09
⏻✸	09 - 11
✸♥♥	11 - 13
⌀♥✸	13 - 15
✈€	15 - 17
♥♥	17 - 19
✸	19 - 21
✈	21 - 23
✸♥	23 - 00

☵☰ 5-Waiting: Be patient and pursue your goal, step by step.

-03:37 EOT 0:00:00 CET/EST	Year *Metal* Month *Wood*	壬寅 Water Tiger Year 壬子 Water Rat Month 壬寅 Winter Solstice

2023	WEEK 1	Water Tiger Year 12. Lunar Month 14. - 17. Day

5TH

癸亥 Water Pig — *Water* — 14:17 ♋

Well — Closing / Opening — 5 - 1/9 - 9

☆☆ ⏻ ❦ ✸ ✈ — until 15:05

☆☆ ♥ — from 15:05

15:05 Slight Cold

✸€	00 - 01
✸	01 - 03
❦♥	03 - 05
₠⏻✹♥	05 - 07
✹❦	07 - 09
✈ϟ	09 - 11
❦	11 - 13
♥	13 - 15
✈₠♥❦	15 - 17
♥❦	17 - 19
∅€	19 - 21
∅✸♥	21 - 23
✸€	23 - 00

9-Small Savings: Go for your ambition with small steps instead of great leaps.

6FR

甲子 Wood Rat — *Metal* — 23:09 ○ ♋

Ghosts — Closing — 5 - 9 - 1

☆ ♥ € ⏻ ❦ ✸

Three Kings' Day

€✹	00 - 01
⏻✹♥	01 - 03
✈€❦	03 - 05
∅♥	05 - 07
♥	07 - 09
✈₠❦	09 - 11
✸❦ϟ	11 - 13
♥❦✹	13 - 15
✸♥	15 - 17
❦	17 - 19
✸	19 - 21
✸♥	21 - 23
€✹	23 - 00

34-Great Strength: Check your handling of power. Grandeur and justice belong together.

7SA

乙丑 Wood Ox — *Metal* — ♋

Willow — Establishment — 5 - 9 - 2

★★★ ♥ ✈ ₠

⏻✹♥	00 - 01
♥✹	01 - 03
✈	03 - 05
❦€	05 - 07
∅	07 - 09
✸♥	09 - 11
✸♥❦	11 - 13
∅₠✸♥ϟ	13 - 15
⏻✹	15 - 17
∅♥	17 - 19
∅✸♥❦	19 - 21
✸✈	21 - 23
⏻✹♥	23 - 00

14-Great Reward: Use your capabilities and assets for common weal.

8SU

丙寅 Fire Tiger — *Fire* — 02:35 ♌

Star — Removal — 5 - 9 - 3

★★★ ❦ ✸ ₠ ∅ ✈

❦✹	00 - 01
∅	01 - 03
✹	03 - 05
♥❦	05 - 07
✸€	07 - 09
∅✸♥❦€	09 - 11
♥	11 - 13
	13 - 15
∅♥✈❦ϟ	15 - 17
₠⏻✹	17 - 19
✸♥	19 - 21
✈₠❦♥	21 - 23
❦✹	23 - 00

43-Severing: Stand up frankly for your own truth. Be determined but not offending.

-04:59 EOT 0:00:00 CET/EST	Year *Metal* Month *Wood*	壬寅 Water Tiger Year 壬子 Water Rat Month 壬寅 Water Tiger Year 壬寅 Water Ox Month Jan 05 15:05

January

2023	WEEK 2	Water Tiger Year 12. Lunar Month 18. - 20. Day

9 MO

丁卯 Fire Rabbit — *Fire* — ♌
Bow — Fulfillment — 5 - 9 - 4

✗✗ ♥ € ✈ ✸

∅♥	00 - 01
∅	01 - 03
✸♥	03 - 05
	05 - 07
♥♥	07 - 09
♥✈	09 - 11
€	11 - 13
♥	13 - 15
✗€	15 - 17
♥⏻✱ϟ	17 - 19
∅✸♥	19 - 21
€⏻♥	21 - 23
∅♥♥	23 - 00

䷫ 44-Meeting: Examine a seductive offer with minuteness and hold off.

10 TU

戊辰 Earth Dragon — *Wood* — 15:01 ♍
Wings — Balance — 5 - 9 - 5

✗✗ ✸ ∅

✸♥	00 - 01
€⏻	01 - 03
✈	03 - 05
∅♥♥✱	05 - 07
∅♥♥	07 - 09
✗	09 - 11
♥	11 - 13
♥✱	13 - 15
€♥	15 - 17
♥	17 - 19
✸ϟ	19 - 21
✸♥	21 - 23
✸♥	23 - 00

䷛ 28-Great Test: Do not blow your plans out of proportions. Be gentle and mind your balance.

11 WE

己巳 Earth Snake — *Wood* — ♍
Carriage — Determination — 5 - 9 - 6

★ ✸

⏻✱♥	00 - 01
♥	01 - 03
✗∅€♥✱	03 - 05
€♥	05 - 07
∅	07 - 09
∅✱	09 - 11
€	11 - 13
	13 - 15
♥	15 - 17
✸	17 - 19
✸€♥	19 - 21
✸✈ϟ	21 - 23
⏻✱	23 - 00

䷱ 50-The Caldron: Sort out material and spiritual ballast and create free space for new ideas.

-06:43 EOT 0:00:00 CET/EST	Year *Metal* Month *Wood*	壬寅 Water Tiger Year 癸丑 Water Ox Month 壬寅 Slight Cold

2023	**WEEK 2**	Water Tiger Year 12. Lunar Month 21. - 24. Day

12TH

庚午 Metal Horse — *Earth* — ♍
Horn — Rigidity — 5 - 9 - 7

★★★

00 - 01
01 - 03
03 - 05
05 - 07
07 - 09
09 - 11
11 - 13
13 - 15
15 - 17
17 - 19
19 - 21
21 - 23
23 - 00

䷟ 32-Constancy: Take up a solid position without freezing.

13FR

辛未 Metal Goat — *Earth* — 02:37 ♎
Neck — Destruction — 5 - 9 - 8

00 - 01
01 - 03
03 - 05
05 - 07
07 - 09
09 - 11
11 - 13
13 - 15
15 - 17
17 - 19
19 - 21
21 - 23
23 - 00

䷸ 57-Penetrating: Get your goals clear and implement them, gentle but consequent.

14SA

壬申 Water Monkey — *Metal* — ♎
Base — Danger — 5 - 9 - 9

00 - 01
01 - 03
03 - 05
05 - 07
07 - 09
09 - 11
11 - 13
13 - 15
15 - 17
17 - 19
19 - 21
21 - 23
23 - 00

䷯ 48-The Well: Develop your potentials and take good care of yourself.

15SU

癸酉 Water Rooster — *Metal* — 02:13 ☾ 11:52 ♏
House — Completion — 5 - 9 - 1

★★★

00 - 01
01 - 03
03 - 05
05 - 07
07 - 09
09 - 11
11 - 13
13 - 15
15 - 17
17 - 19
19 - 21
21 - 23
23 - 00

䷑ 18-Decaying: Do not be too good for humble work. Clear backlog.

-07:55 EOT 0:00:00 CET/EST	Year *Metal* Month *Wood*	壬寅 Water Tiger Year 癸丑 Water Ox Month 壬寅 Slight Cold

January

2023	**WEEK 3**	Water Tiger Year 12. Lunar Month 25. - 27. Day

16 MO

甲戌 Wood Dog — *Fire* — ♏
Heart — Harvest — 5 - 9 - 2

★★ ♥ € ✗

♥	00 - 01
€♥✱	01 - 03
€♥♥	03 - 05
⌀♥	05 - 07
ϟ	07 - 09
♥	09 - 11
✱♥	11 - 13
♥♥✱	13 - 15
✱✈€	15 - 17
♥♥	17 - 19
✱	19 - 21
✗€	21 - 23
♥	23 - 00

䷭ 46-Rising: Rely on your intuition. Put your plans into action - now.

17 TU

乙亥 Wood Pig — *Fire* — 17:24 ♐
Tail — Opening — 5 - 9 - 3

★★★ ♥

⏻✱	00 - 01
	01 - 03
♥♥	03 - 05
♥	05 - 07
♥	07 - 09
⌀✱✈ϟ	09 - 11
✱	11 - 13
✱♥	13 - 15
✗€♥♥⏻	15 - 17
✱♥♥	17 - 19
⌀€♥	19 - 21
⌀♥	21 - 23
⏻✱	23 - 00

䷅ 6-Litigating:
Be honest but not stubborn or impolite. Solve a conflict with empathy and compromising.

18 WE

丙子 Fire Rat — *Water* — ♐
Basket — Closing — 5 - 9 - 4

✗ ♥ € ⏻ ♥ ✱

€✱	00 - 01
♥	01 - 03
✈	03 - 05
⌀♥♥	05 - 07
✱♥	07 - 09
✗✱	09 - 11
♥ϟ	11 - 13
⌀♥♥	13 - 15
✱♥♥	15 - 17
♥⏻	17 - 19
	19 - 21
♥⏻✱	21 - 23
€✱	23 - 00

䷮ 47-Confining: Benefit from your problems for your progress but do not talk about it.

-09:24 EOT 0:00:00 CET/EST	Year *Metal* Month *Wood*	壬寅 Water Tiger Year 癸丑 Water Ox Month 壬寅 Slight Cold

2023	WEEK 3	Water Tiger Year 12. Lunar Month 28. - 30. Day Water Rabbit Year 1. Lunar Month 1. Day

19TH

丁丑 Fire Ox — *Water* — 19:08 Capricorn

Dipper — Establishment — 5 - 9 - 5

00 - 01
01 - 03
03 - 05
05 - 07
07 - 09
09 - 11
11 - 13
13 - 15
15 - 17
17 - 19
19 - 21
21 - 23
23 - 00

64-Not Yet Accomplished: Specify precisely what you want to start but finish it definitely.

20FR

戊寅 Earth Tiger — *Earth* — Capricorn

Ox — Removal — 5 - 9 - 6

08:30 Great Cold

00 - 01
01 - 03
03 - 05
05 - 07
07 - 09
09 - 11
11 - 13
13 - 15
15 - 17
17 - 19
19 - 21
21 - 23
23 - 00

40-Separating: Disengage yourself from dead weight and return to your roots. Complete necessary objectives immediately.

21SA

己卯 Earth Rabbit — *Earth* — 20:55 ● 18:29 Aquarius

Maiden — Fulfillment — 5 - 9 - 7

00 - 01
01 - 03
03 - 05
05 - 07
07 - 09
09 - 11
11 - 13
13 - 15
15 - 17
17 - 19
19 - 21
21 - 23
23 - 00

59-Dispersing: Break deadlocked structures with changes and shared joy.

22SU

庚辰 Metal Dragon — *Metal* — Aquarius

Void — Balance — 5 - 9 - 8

Chinese New Year

00 - 01
01 - 03
03 - 05
05 - 07
07 - 09
09 - 11
11 - 13
13 - 15
15 - 17
17 - 19
19 - 21
21 - 23
23 - 00

29-Cavern: Be truly and sincere to yourself. Overcome obstacles peacefully.

-10:23 EOT 0:00:00 CET/EST	Year *Metal* Month *Wood*	壬寅 Water Tiger Year 癸丑 Water Ox Month 壬寅 Great Cold Jan 20 08:30

January

2023	**WEEK 4**	Water Rabbit Year 1. Lunar Month 2. - 4. Day

23MO

辛巳 Metal Snake — *Metal* — 17:40 ♓
Roof — Determination — 5 - 9 - 9

★ ⏻ ✸

	00 - 01
♥	01 - 03
✗€♥♥✸	03 - 05
€♥	05 - 07
⌀✸	07 - 09
⌀	09 - 11
⏻✸	11 - 13
✸	13 - 15
⌀✸	15 - 17
✸€	17 - 19
€	19 - 21
✈ϟ	21 - 23
	23 - 00

☲ 4-Ignorance: Be enthusiastic and open minded but rely on your experience.

24^TU

壬午 Water Horse — *Wood* — ♓
Room — Rigidity — 5 - 9 - 1

★★★ ♥♥✗

♥€ϟ	00 - 01
⌀♥♥✸	01 - 03
✸♥	03 - 05
♥⏻	05 - 07
	07 - 09
€⏻✸	09 - 11
⌀✸♥♥	11 - 13
⌀✸♥♥	13 - 15
✸✈	15 - 17
✸	17 - 19
♥	19 - 21
✗♥	21 - 23
♥€ϟ	23 - 00

☰ 33-Retiring: A retreat in the right moment saves your dignity. Be insistent.

25^WE

癸未 Water Goat — *Wood* — 18:57 ♈
Wall — Destruction — 5 - 9 - 2

★★★ϟ ♥✸⌀

✸♥♥€	00 - 01
⌀✸♥ϟ	01 - 03
€	03 - 05
⏻✸♥	05 - 07
✸♥	07 - 09
✈⏻	09 - 11
♥♥	11 - 13
€✸	13 - 15
✗€✸	15 - 17
⌀✸♥	17 - 19
⌀♥♥	19 - 21
✸♥	21 - 23
✸♥♥€	23 - 00

☱ 31-Influencing:
Reconcile your ambitions and your needs. Use the natural power of attraction of all things.

-11:32 EOT 0:00:00 CET/EST	Year *Metal* Month *Wood*	壬寅 Water Tiger Year 癸丑 Water Ox Month 壬寅 Great Cold

2023	WEEK 4	Water Rabbit Year 1. Lunar Month 5. - 8. Day

January

26TH

甲申 Wood Monkey — *Water* — ♈
Astride — Danger — 5 - 9 - 3

★ϟ € ♥♥ ✹

♥	00 - 01
⏻ ✹	01 - 03
∅ ♥ ✈ € ♥♥ ϟ	03 - 05
♥	05 - 07
€ ♥	07 - 09
✈ ∅ €	09 - 11
✹ ♥♥	11 - 13
	13 - 15
	15 - 17
€	17 - 19
	19 - 21
∅ ♥ ♥♥	21 - 23
♥	23 - 00

56-Traveling: Scoop from your inner source, be attentive and start for new shore.

27FR

乙酉 Wood Rooster — *Water* — 23:59 ♉
Rope — Completion — 5 - 9 - 4

★★★ ♥♥ ♥ ✹ € ⏻ ✈

♥♥ ⏻ ✹	00 - 01
∅ ♥	01 - 03
✈ €	03 - 05
♥♥ € ϟ	05 - 07
∅ ♥ ♥♥	07 - 09
✹	09 - 11
✹ €	11 - 13
✹	13 - 15
⏻ ✹	15 - 17
∅ ♥	17 - 19
♥	19 - 21
€ ✈	21 - 23
♥♥ ⏻ ✹	23 - 00

62-Small Testing: Concentrate on the details and complete them with accuracy.

28SA

丙戌 Fire Dog — *Earth* — 15:20 ☽ — ♉
Stomach — Harvest — 5 - 9 - 5

☆☆ ♥♥ € ✈

♥♥ ✹	00 - 01
∅ € ♥	01 - 03
♥	03 - 05
∅ ♥ ♥♥	05 - 07
✹ ϟ	07 - 09
✹ €	09 - 11
✹ ♥	11 - 13
∅ ✹ ♥ ♥♥	13 - 15
✈ € ♥♥	15 - 17
♥ ♥♥ ⏻ ✹	17 - 19
✹	19 - 21
✈ € ⏻ ✹	21 - 23
♥♥ ✹	23 - 00

53-Gradually Progressing: Achieve your plans, patient and with integrity.

29SU

丁亥 Fire Pig — *Earth* — ♉
Pleiades — Opening — 5 - 9 - 6

★★ ♥ ✹

	00 - 01
	01 - 03
✹ ♥	03 - 05
€ ✹ ♥	05 - 07
	07 - 09
∅ ✈ ϟ	09 - 11
✹ € ♥♥	11 - 13
✹ ♥	13 - 15
✈ € ♥ ♥♥	15 - 17
♥ ♥♥ ⏻ ✹	17 - 19
∅ €	19 - 21
♥ ✹	21 - 23
♥♥	23 - 00

39-Obstructing: Do not bash your head against a wall. Retreat, bethink and talk to friends.

-12:16 EOT 0:00:00 CET/EST	Year *Metal* Month *Wood*	壬寅 Water Tiger Year 癸丑 Water Ox Month 壬寅 Great Cold

2023	WEEK 5	Water Rabbit Year 1. Lunar Month 9. - 11. Day

30 MO

戊子 Earth Rat — *Fire* — 08:55 ♊
Net — Closing — 5 - 9 - 7

⌀ ♥ € ⏻ ✸

€	00 - 01
⏻ ♥ ♥	01 - 03
✈	03 - 05
⌀ ♥ ✸	05 - 07
♥ ♥	07 - 09
✗	09 - 11
✸ ♥ ϟ	11 - 13
♥ ♥	13 - 15
♥	15 - 17
♥	17 - 19
✸	19 - 21
✸ ♥ ♥	21 - 23
€	23 - 00

☶ 52-Stopping: Make peace with your core and do not get disturbed by emotions.

31 TU

己丑 Earth Ox — *Fire* — ♊
Beak — Establishment — 5 - 9 - 8

★★★ ♥ ✈ €

⏻ ✸ ♥ ♥	00 - 01
♥ ✸	01 - 03
✗ ✸ ♥	03 - 05
♥	05 - 07
⌀ ♥	07 - 09
♥	09 - 11
✸ ♥ ♥ €	11 - 13
⌀ € ✸ ♥ ϟ	13 - 15
⏻	15 - 17
⌀ ✸ ♥	17 - 19
⌀ ♥ ♥	19 - 21
✈	21 - 23
⏻ ✸ ♥	23 - 00

䷎ 15-Modesty: Be modest but not humble or self-deprecating. Engage in common cause.

1 WE

庚寅 Metal Tiger — *Wood* — 20:27 ♋
Orion — Removal — 5 - 9 - 9

★★★ ♥ € ✗

♥	00 - 01
✸	01 - 03
✸	03 - 05
♥	05 - 07
€	07 - 09
⌀ ♥ ♥	09 - 11
♥	11 - 13
⏻	13 - 15
⌀ ✸ ♥ ✈ € ϟ	15 - 17
€ ♥	17 - 19
♥ ♥	19 - 21
✗ ⌀ € ♥ ♥	21 - 23
♥	23 - 00

䷋ 12-Adversity: Keep your balance and listen to your heart. Savor everyday commodities.

-13:03 EOT 0:00:00 CET/EST	Year *Metal* Month *Wood*	壬寅 Water Tiger Year 癸丑 Water Ox Month 壬寅 Great Cold

2 TH

辛卯 Metal Rabbit — *Wood* — ♋

Well — Fulfillment — 5 - 9 - 1

★

00 - 01
01 - 03
03 - 05
05 - 07
07 - 09
09 - 11
11 - 13
13 - 15
15 - 17
17 - 19
19 - 21
21 - 23
23 - 00

45-Gathering: Personal sacrifices foster your personal up growth.

3 FR

壬辰 Water Dragon — *Water* — ♋

Ghosts — Balance — 5 - 9 - 2

★★

00 - 01
01 - 03
03 - 05
05 - 07
07 - 09
09 - 11
11 - 13
13 - 15
15 - 17
17 - 19
19 - 21
21 - 23
23 - 00

35-Promoting: Be upright, noble and generous. The lust for life evolves from good deeds.

4 SA

癸巳 Water Snake — *Water* — 08:55 ♌

Willow — Determination / Balance — 5/4 - 9/8 - 3

★★ — until 02:43

from 02:43

02:43 Coming of Spring

00 - 01
01 - 03
03 - 05
05 - 07
07 - 09
09 - 11
11 - 13
13 - 15
15 - 17
17 - 19
19 - 21
21 - 23
23 - 00

16-Satisfying: Pass your enthusiasm to others. Together you will succeed faster.

5 SU

甲午 Wood Horse — *Metal* — 18:30 ○ — ♌

Star — Determination — 4 - 8 - 4

★★★

00 - 01
01 - 03
03 - 05
05 - 07
07 - 09
09 - 11
11 - 13
13 - 15
15 - 17
17 - 19
19 - 21
21 - 23
23 - 00

20-Observing: Take the time to take personal stock as a basis for your spiritual growth.

-13:30 EOT 0:00:00 CET/EST	Year *Metal* Month *Wood*	壬寅 Water Tiger Year 癸丑 Water Ox Month 癸卯 Water Rabbit Year 癸卯 Wood Tiger Month Feb 04 02:43

2023	**WEEK 6**	Water Rabbit Year 1. Lunar Month 16. - 18. Day

6 MO

乙未 Wood Goat — *Metal* — 21:12 ♍

Bow — Rigidity — 4 - 8 - 5

✫✫ ❤✶

♥❤⏻✸	00 - 01
∅♥ϟ	01 - 03
€	03 - 05
€♥	05 - 07
✸❤	07 - 09
✸✈	09 - 11
✸♥	11 - 13
₠	13 - 15
✶₠⏻✸	15 - 17
∅❤	17 - 19
∅♥	19 - 21
♥	21 - 23
♥❤⏻✸	23 - 00

䷇ 8-Alliance: Do not hesitate to act jointly.

7 TU

丙申 Fire Monkey — *Fire* — ♍

Wings — Destruction — 4 - 8 - 6

✫ϟ ♥₠

✸♥	00 - 01
	01 - 03
∅♥✈ϟ	03 - 05
♥❤	05 - 07
✸€♥	07 - 09
✶∅✸❤	09 - 11
❤	11 - 13
∅	13 - 15
✸❤	15 - 17
₠⏻✸	17 - 19
	19 - 21
♥❤✸	21 - 23
✸♥	23 - 00

䷖ 23-Stripping: Dark clouds are rising. Retreat and bethink yourself.

8 WE

丁酉 Fire Rooster — *Fire* — ♍

Carriage — Danger — 4 - 8 - 7

★★★ϟ ⏻ ❤✶

❤	00 - 01
∅♥	01 - 03
✶₠✸❤	03 - 05
✸❤ϟ	05 - 07
∅✸♥	07 - 09
✸	09 - 11
€❤	11 - 13
	13 - 15
	15 - 17
♥✸	17 - 19
♥❤	19 - 21
₠✈⏻✸	21 - 23
	23 - 00

䷗ 24-Returning: Something re-enters your life. Clarify your ambitions to get a good start.

-13:54 EOT 0:00:00 CET/EST	Year *Metal* Month *Water*	癸卯 Water Rabbit Year 甲寅 Wood Tiger Month 癸卯 Coming of Spring

2023	WEEK 6	Water Rabbit Year 1. Lunar Month 19. - 22. Day

February

✸❣ 00 - 01	**9TH**	戊戌 Earth Dog — *Wood* — 08:38 ♎
€̸❥❣ 01 - 03		Horn — Completion — 4 - 8 - 8
♥ 03 - 05	∅∅ϟ	❣ ♥ ✸ ✈
∅✸♥ 05 - 07		
✸❣ϟ 07 - 09		
✸€ 09 - 11		
♥ 11 - 13		
❥❣✸ 13 - 15		
✈€ 15 - 17		
❥❣ 17 - 19		
19 - 21		
✈̸€̸✸❣ 21 - 23		
✸❣ 23 - 00		䷚ 27-Jaws: Take care of your corporal and mental nourishment.

⏻✸❣ 00 - 01	**10FR**	己亥 Earth Pig — *Wood* — ♎
01 - 03		Neck — Harvest — 4 - 8 - 9
✸♥ 03 - 05	★	♥ ⏻ ✈̸
€̸♥ 05 - 07		
✸ 07 - 09		
∅✸✈ϟ 09 - 11		
€ 11 - 13		
♥ 13 - 15		
✈̸€̸❥❣⏻ 15 - 17		
✸❥❣ 17 - 19		
∅€❣ 19 - 21		
∅❥ 21 - 23		
⏻✸ 23 - 00		䷂ 3-Accumulating: The start is difficult. Be patient and accept help. You will be successful.

€✸ 00 - 01	**11SA**	庚子 Metal Rat — *Earth* — 18:21 ♏
⏻✸♥ 01 - 03		Base — Opening — 4 - 8 - 1
✈ 03 - 05	★	♥ € ✈ ✸
∅❥ 05 - 07		
✸❥ 07 - 09		
✈̸€̸✸ 09 - 11		
❣ϟ 11 - 13		
❥❣ 13 - 15		
✸€♥ 15 - 17		
17 - 19		
❣ 19 - 21		
❥ 21 - 23		
€✸ 23 - 00		䷩ 42-Increasing: Use your abilities for common welfare. Learn from mistakes.

♥ 00 - 01	**12SU**	辛丑 Metal Ox — *Earth* — ♏
❥✸ 01 - 03		House — Closing — 4 - 8 - 2
✈̸⏻✸ 03 - 05	∅	✸
❣ 05 - 07		
∅✸❣ 07 - 09		
♥ 09 - 11		
❥❣⏻✸ 11 - 13		
∅€̸✸❥ϟ 13 - 15		
❣ 15 - 17		
∅€♥ 17 - 19		
∅❥ 19 - 21		
✈ 21 - 23		
♥ 23 - 00		䷲ 51-Startling: A change is imminent. Keep your calmness and humor, everything will turn to good account.

-14:04 EOT 0:00:00 CET/EST	Year *Metal* Month *Water*	癸卯 Water Rabbit Year 甲寅 Wood Tiger Month 癸卯 Coming of Spring

February

2023	**WEEK 7**	Water Rabbit Year 1. Lunar Month 23. - 25. Day

13 MO

壬寅 Water Tiger *Metal* 16:03 ☾ ♏
Heart Establishment 4 - 8 - 3

★ ♥ ⏻ ✈

♥	00 - 01
⌀ ✸	01 - 03
	03 - 05
♥ ⏻	05 - 07
✸ €	07 - 09
♥ ♥	09 - 11
✸ ♥ ♥	11 - 13
✸ ♥	13 - 15
⌀ ♥ ✈ ϟ	15 - 17
€	17 - 19
♥	19 - 21
✈ ⌀ ♥ ♥	21 - 23
♥	23 - 00

䷔ 21-Gnawing And Chewing: Conquer difficulties with discipline and justice.

14 TU

癸卯 Water Rabbit *Metal* 01:20 ♐
Tail Removal 4 - 8 - 4

★ ♥ ⌀ ✈
Valentine's Day

⌀ ✸ ♥ €	00 - 01
⌀ ✸	01 - 03
	03 - 05
⏻ ✸	05 - 07
♥	07 - 09
♥ ✈ ⏻	09 - 11
€	11 - 13
♥	13 - 15
✈ €	15 - 17
♥ ϟ	17 - 19
⌀ ♥	19 - 21
€ ✸ ♥	21 - 23
⌀ ✸ ♥ €	23 - 00

䷐ 17-Following: Learn everything from the scratch and accept advice. This is the basis of authority and recognition.

15 WE

甲辰 Wood Dragon *Fire* ♐
Basket Fulfillment 4 - 8 - 5

☆☆ ♥ € ✈ ♥ ✸

♥	00 - 01
€ ♥ ⏻ ✸	01 - 03
✸ ✈ € ♥	03 - 05
⌀ ✸ ♥ ♥	05 - 07
⌀ ♥	07 - 09
✈ € ♥	09 - 11
✸ ♥	11 - 13
♥ ✸	13 - 15
✸ € ♥	15 - 17
♥	17 - 19
ϟ	19 - 21
	21 - 23
♥	23 - 00

䷘ 25-Without Wrongdoing: Follow your intuition without calculating intention.

-14:06 EOT 0:00:00 CET/EST	Year *Metal* Month *Water*	癸卯 Water Rabbit Year 甲寅 Wood Tiger Month 癸卯 Coming of Spring

2023	WEEK 7	Water Rabbit Year 1. Lunar Month 26. - 29. Day

16TH

乙巳 Wood Snake — *Fire* — 04:55 ♑

Dipper — Balance — 4 - 8 - 6

00 - 01
01 - 03
03 - 05
05 - 07
07 - 09
09 - 11
11 - 13
13 - 15
15 - 17
17 - 19
19 - 21
21 - 23
23 - 00

36-Brightness Wounded: Hide your light under a bushel and persecute your aim.

17FR

丙午 Fire Horse — *Water* — ♑

Ox — Determination — 4 - 8 - 7

★★★

00 - 01
01 - 03
03 - 05
05 - 07
07 - 09
09 - 11
11 - 13
13 - 15
15 - 17
17 - 19
19 - 21
21 - 23
23 - 00

22-Adorning: Design everything functional and beautiful because beauty fosters function.

18SA

丁未 Fire Goat — *Water* — 05:34 ♒

Maiden — Rigidity — 4 - 8 - 8

★

22:35 Rain Water

00 - 01
01 - 03
03 - 05
05 - 07
07 - 09
09 - 11
11 - 13
13 - 15
15 - 17
17 - 19
19 - 21
21 - 23
23 - 00

63-Already Accomplished: An end is achieved. Finish accurately and prepare for the next begin.

19SU

戊申 Earth Monkey — *Earth* — ♒

Void — Destruction — 4 - 8 - 9

00 - 01
01 - 03
03 - 05
05 - 07
07 - 09
09 - 11
11 - 13
13 - 15
15 - 17
17 - 19
19 - 21
21 - 23
23 - 00

37-Family: Be reliable and consolidate the output as a solid platform for further developments.

-13:59 EOT 0:00:00 CET/EST	Year *Metal* Month *Water*	癸卯 Water Rabbit Year 甲寅 Wood Tiger Month 癸卯 Rain Water Feb 18 22:35

February

February

2023	WEEK 8	Water Rabbit Year 2. Lunar Month 1. - 3. Day

⏻✹ 00 - 01	**20**MO	己酉 Earth Rooster *Earth* 07:09 ● 04:57 ♓
∅♥ 01 - 03		Roof Danger 4 - 8 - 1
⚹€❤ 03 - 05	∅⚡	✹⚹
✹❤⚡ 05 - 07		Rose Monday
∅♥ 07 - 09		
09 - 11		
€ 11 - 13		
13 - 15		
⏻ 15 - 17		
∅✹♥ 17 - 19		
♥ 19 - 21		
€✈ 21 - 23		
❤⏻✹ 23 - 00	䷶	55-Overshadowing: Use your wealth with wisdom for your ambitions.

❤ 00 - 01	**21**TU	庚戌 Metal Dog *Metal* ♓
€♥✹ 01 - 03		Room Completion 4 - 8 - 2
✹♥ 03 - 05	★	❤ ♥ € ✈
∅✹♥ 05 - 07		
⚡ 07 - 09		
09 - 11		
♥ 11 - 13		
♥❤ 13 - 15		
✹✈€ 15 - 17		
♥ 17 - 19		
✹❤ 19 - 21		
⚹€ 21 - 23		
❤ 23 - 00	䷝	30-Brightness: Light your inner fire. Enlighten dark corners and unsettled affairs.

00 - 01	**22**WE	辛亥 Metal Pig *Metal* 05:15 ♈
01 - 03		Wall Harvest 4 - 8 - 3
❤⏻♥ 03 - 05	★	♥ ⏻ ⚹
€✹♥ 05 - 07		Ash Wednesday
✹ 07 - 09		
∅✈⚡ 09 - 11		
⏻✹ 11 - 13		
✹♥ 13 - 15		
⚹€♥ 15 - 17		
♥❤€ 17 - 19		
∅€ 19 - 21		
∅♥ 21 - 23		
23 - 00	䷰	49-Reforming: It is a convenient time for changes. Trust in your competence be persistent.

-13:41 EOT 0:00:00 CET/EST	Year *Metal* Month *Water*	癸卯 Water Rabbit Year 甲寅 Wood Tiger Month 癸卯 Rain Water

2023	**WEEK 8**	Water Rabbit Year 2. Lunar Month 4. - 7. Day

23TH

壬子 Water Rat — *Wood* — ♈

Astride — Opening — 4 - 8 - 4

★ ♥ € ✈ ✸

- €✸ 00 - 01
- ✸♥ 01 - 03
- ✸✈ 03 - 05
- ♥ 05 - 07
- ♥ 07 - 09
- ✈€⏻✸ 09 - 11
- ✸ϟ 11 - 13
- ∅♥✸ 13 - 15
- ♥ 15 - 17
- ♥ 17 - 19
- 19 - 21
- ♥€ 21 - 23
- €✸ 23 - 00

䷒ 19-Arriving: Seize the opportunity. Invest in your future.

24FR

癸丑 Water Ox — *Wood* — 08:35 ♉

Rope — Closing — 4 - 8 - 5

☆☆ ✸

- ✸€♥ 00 - 01
- ♥ 01 - 03
- ✈✸ 03 - 05
- ♥⏻ 05 - 07
- ∅✸ 07 - 09
- ⏻♥ 09 - 11
- ♥ 11 - 13
- ∅€♥ϟ 13 - 15
- 15 - 17
- ∅♥ 17 - 19
- ∅♥ 19 - 21
- ✸✈ 21 - 23
- ✸€♥ 23 - 00

䷨ 41-Decreasing: Affiliate honesty with self-restraint. Small things provoke big ones.

25SA

甲寅 Wood Tiger — *Water* — ♉

Stomach — Establishment — 4 - 8 - 6

☆☆ ♥ ⏻ ✈

- ✸♥ 00 - 01
- 01 - 03
- €✸♥ 03 - 05
- ♥ 05 - 07
- € 07 - 09
- ∅♥ 09 - 11
- ✸♥ 11 - 13
- ⏻✸ 13 - 15
- ∅✸♥✈ϟ 15 - 17
- € 17 - 19
- ♥ 19 - 21
- ✈∅€♥♥ 21 - 23
- ✸♥ 23 - 00

䷻ 60-Regulating: Identify your limitations. Extend suffocating ones, establish wise ones.

26SU

乙卯 Wood Rabbit — *Water* — 16:03 ♊

Pleiades — Removal — 4 - 8 - 7

★ ♥∅✈

- ♥ 00 - 01
- ∅✸ 01 - 03
- 03 - 05
- €✸ 05 - 07
- ♥ 07 - 09
- ✸♥✈ 09 - 11
- ✸♥€ 11 - 13
- ✸♥ 13 - 15
- ✈€⏻✸ 15 - 17
- ♥ϟ 17 - 19
- ∅♥♥ 19 - 21
- €♥ 21 - 23
- ♥ 23 - 00

䷼ 61-Mutually Trusting: Have an open mind and search for the true core. This arises understanding, adjacency and continuance.

-13:20 EOT 0:00:00 CET/EST	Year *Metal* Month *Water*	癸卯 Water Rabbit Year 甲寅 Wood Tiger Month 癸卯 Rain Water

February

February

2023	**WEEK 9**	Water Rabbit Year 2. Lunar Month 8. - 10. Day

27 MO

丙辰 Fire Dragon — *Earth* — 08:06 ☽ — ♊

Net — Fulfillment — 4 - 8 - 8

★ ♥ € ⏻ ✈ ♥

- ♥ 00 - 01
- € ✸ ♥ 01 - 03
- ✈ 03 - 05
- Ø ♥ 05 - 07
- Ø ✸ ♥ 07 - 09
- ✶ ✸ 09 - 11
- ♥ 11 - 13
- Ø ♥ 13 - 15
- € ♥ ♥ 15 - 17
- ⏻ ✸ ♥ 17 - 19
- ⚡ 19 - 21
- ⏻ ✸ 21 - 23
- ♥ 23 - 00

☳☱ 54-The Libidinal Addiction: Be true to your emotions and addiction but with retention.

28 TU

丁巳 Fire Snake — *Earth* — ♊

Beak — Balance — 4 - 8 - 9

☆ ✈ ♥

- ✸ 00 - 01
- ✸ ♥ 01 - 03
- ✶ Ø € ✸ ♥ 03 - 05
- € ✸ ♥ 05 - 07
- Ø 07 - 09
- Ø ✸ 09 - 11
- € ♥ 11 - 13
- 13 - 15
- Ø ♥ 15 - 17
- ⏻ ✸ 17 - 19
- € 19 - 21
- ✈ ⏻ ✸ ⚡ 21 - 23
- ✸ ♥ 23 - 00

☲☱ 38-Misunderstanding:
Remain true to yourself. Develop individual differences to constructive connections.

1 WE

戊午 Earth Horse — *Fire* — 03:02 ♋

Orion — Determination — 4 - 8 - 1

★★★

- ✸ ♥ € ⚡ 00 - 01
- ♥ 01 - 03
- ♥ 03 - 05
- ♥ ✸ 05 - 07
- ♥ 07 - 09
- 09 - 11
- Ø ♥ 11 - 13
- ✸ ♥ 13 - 15
- ✈ 15 - 17
- 17 - 19
- ✸ ♥ 19 - 21
- ✶ € ✸ ♥ ♥ 21 - 23
- ✸ ♥ € ⚡ 23 - 00

☱☱ 58-Pleasing: With an inner smile about yourself and the world you will win the hearts of other people and free your own.

-12:43 EOT 0:00:00 CET/EST	Year *Metal* Month *Water*	癸卯 Water Rabbit Year 甲寅 Wood Tiger Month 癸卯 Rain Water

2023	**WEEK 9**	Water Rabbit Year 2. Lunar Month 11. - 14. Day

2TH

己未 Earth Goat — *Fire* — ♋
Well — Rigidity — 4 - 8 - 2

✫✫ ✈

♥⏻	00 - 01
∅✸♥ϟ	01 - 03
€✸♥	03 - 05
♥	05 - 07
	07 - 09
✈	09 - 11
€♥	11 - 13
€✸	13 - 15
✈€⏻	15 - 17
∅✸♥	17 - 19
∅♥	19 - 21
♥	21 - 23
♥♥⏻	23 - 00

☰ 10-Treading: Show self-confidence and inner strength together with sereneness.

3FR

庚申 Metal Monkey — *Wood* — 15:33 ♌
Ghosts — Destruction — 4 - 8 - 3

✫✫ϟ ♥✸€∅

✸♥	00 - 01
⏻	01 - 03
∅♥✈ϟ	03 - 05
♥	05 - 07
€♥	07 - 09
✈∅€♥	09 - 11
♥	11 - 13
	13 - 15
€	15 - 17
€♥	17 - 19
♥	19 - 21
∅♥♥	21 - 23
✸♥	23 - 00

☰ 11-Prominence: Work together and complement one another. Everyone will profit.

4SA

辛酉 Metal Rooster — *Wood* — ♌
Willow — Danger — 4 - 8 - 4

✫✫ϟ ♥✸✈

✸♥	00 - 01
∅✸♥	01 - 03
✈€⏻✸	03 - 05
♥ϟ	05 - 07
∅✸♥	07 - 09
	09 - 11
⏻€✸	11 - 13
✸	13 - 15
♥	15 - 17
∅♥€	17 - 19
♥♥	19 - 21
€✈	21 - 23
✸♥	23 - 00

☰ 26-Great Gains: Focus your strength. Go out and utilize your capabilities profitably.

5SU

壬戌 Water Dog — *Water* — ♌
Star — Completion / Danger — 4 - 8/7 - 5

✫✫ ♥♥✸€✈ — until 20:37
✫✫ ♥ ♥✸∅✈ — from 20:37
20:37 Waking of Worms

✸♥	00 - 01
∅€♥	01 - 03
✸♥	03 - 05
♥	05 - 07
ϟ	07 - 09
⏻✸	09 - 11
✸♥♥	11 - 13
∅♥✸	13 - 15
✈€	15 - 17
♥♥	17 - 19
✸	19 - 21
✈	21 - 23
✸♥	23 - 00

☰ 5-Waiting: Be patient and pursue your goal, step by step.

-12:10 EOT 0:00:00 CET/EST	Year *Metal* Month *Water*	癸卯 Water Rabbit Year 甲寅 Wood Tiger Month 癸卯 Water Rabbit Year 癸卯 Wood Rabbit Month Mar 05 20:37

Preview 2023

March 2023

Day	Note	Moon
1 We		
2 Th		
3 Fr		
4 Sa		
5 Su		
6 Mo		
7 Tu		○
8 We		
9 Th		
10 Fr		
11 Sa		
12 Su		
13 Mo		
14 Tu		
15 We		☾
16 Th		
17 Fr		
18 Sa		
19 Su		
20 Mo		
21 Tu		●
22 We		
23 Th		
24 Fr		
25 Sa		
26 Su		
27 Mo		
28 Tu		
29 We		☽
30 Th		
31 Fr		

April 2023

Day	Note	Moon
1 Sa		
2 Su		
3 Mo		
4 Tu		
5 We		
6 Th		○
7 Fr	Good Friday	
8 Sa		
9 Su	Easter Sunday	
10 Mo	Easter Monday	
11 Tu		
12 We		
13 Th		☾
14 Fr		
15 Sa		
16 Su		
17 Mo		
18 Tu		
19 We		
20 Th		●
21 Fr		
22 Sa		
23 Su		
24 Mo		
25 Tu		
26 We		
27 Th		☽
28 Fr		
29 Sa		
30 Su		

May 2023

Day	Note	Moon
1 Mo	Labour Day	
2 Tu		
3 We		
4 Th		
5 Fr		○
6 Sa		
7 Su		
8 Mo		
9 Tu		
10 We		
11 Th		
12 Fr		☾
13 Sa		
14 Su		
15 Mo		
16 Tu		
17 We		
18 Th	Ascension	
19 Fr		●
20 Sa		
21 Su		
22 Mo		
23 Tu		
24 We		
25 Th		
26 Fr		
27 Sa		☽
28 Su	Whit Sunday	
29 Mo	Whit Monday	
30 Tu		
31 We		

Preview 2023

June 2023

1 Th
2 Fr
3 Sa
4 Su ○
5 Mo
6 Tu
7 We
8 Th
9 Fr
10 Sa ☾
11 Su
12 Mo
13 Tu
14 We
15 Th
16 Fr
17 Sa
18 Su ●
19 Mo
20 Tu
21 We
22 Th
23 Fr
24 Sa
25 Su
26 Mo ☽
27 Tu
28 We
29 Th
30 Fr

July 2023

1 Sa
2 Su
3 Mo ○
4 Tu
5 We
6 Th
7 Fr
8 Sa
9 Su
10 Mo ☾
11 Tu
12 We
13 Th
14 Fr
15 Sa
16 Su
17 Mo ●
18 Tu
19 We
20 Th
21 Fr
22 Sa
23 Su
24 Mo
25 Tu ☽
26 We
27 Th
28 Fr
29 Sa
30 Su
31 Mo

August 2023

1 Tu ○
2 We
3 Th
4 Fr
5 Sa
6 Su
7 Mo
8 Tu ☾
9 We
10 Th
11 Fr
12 Sa
13 Su
14 Mo
15 Tu
16 We ●
17 Th
18 Fr
19 Sa
20 Su
21 Mo
22 Tu
23 We
24 Th ☽
25 Fr
26 Sa
27 Su
28 Mo
29 Tu
30 We
31 Th ○

Preview

Preview 2023

September 2023

1	Fr	
2	Sa	
3	Su	
4	Mo	
5	Tu	
6	We	☾
7	Th	
8	Fr	
9	Sa	
10	Su	
11	Mo	
12	Tu	
13	We	
14	Th	
15	Fr	●
16	Sa	
17	Su	
18	Mo	
19	Tu	
20	We	
21	Th	
22	Fr	☽
23	Sa	
24	Su	
25	Mo	
26	Tu	
27	We	
28	Th	
29	Fr	○
30	Sa	

October 2023

1	Su	
2	Mo	
3	Tu	
4	We	
5	Th	
6	Fr	☾
7	Sa	
8	Su	
9	Mo	
10	Tu	
11	We	
12	Th	
13	Fr	
14	Sa	●
15	Su	
16	Mo	
17	Tu	
18	We	
19	Th	
20	Fr	
21	Sa	
22	Su	☽
23	Mo	
24	Tu	
25	We	
26	Th	
27	Fr	
28	Sa	○
29	Su	
30	Mo	
31	Tu	Halloween

November 2023

1	We	
2	Th	
3	Fr	
4	Sa	
5	Su	☾
6	Mo	
7	Tu	
8	We	
9	Th	
10	Fr	
11	Sa	
12	Su	
13	Mo	●
14	Tu	
15	We	
16	Th	
17	Fr	
18	Sa	
19	Su	
20	Mo	☽
21	Tu	
22	We	
23	Th	
24	Fr	
25	Sa	
26	Su	
27	Mo	○
28	Tu	
29	We	
30	Th	

December 2023

1 Fr

2 Sa

3 Su 1. Advent

4 Mo

5 Tu ☾

6 We Saint Nicholas

7 Th

8 Fr

9 Sa

10 Su 2. Advent

11 Mo

12 Tu ●

13 We

14 Th

15 Fr

16 Sa

17 Su 3. Advent

18 Mo

19 Tu ☽

20 We

21 Th

22 Fr

23 Sa

24 Su Christmas Eve 4....

25 Mo Christmas

26 Tu

27 We ○

28 Th

29 Fr

30 Sa

31 Su New Year's Eve

2024

2025

Chinese Calendar

Since human beings exist, they looked up to the sky. They observed the periodicity of natural phenomena. The firmament was their clock. The stars were the dial, with sun and moon as hands.

The base of all known calendars are the alternation of day and night, the phases of the moon and the succession of the seasons. They define the periods of hour, day, month and year.

Month and year, being based on solstices and equinoxes respectively full moon and new moon, are defined by the movement of the celestial bodies in space. These events take place at a specific point in time, so they are independent from any location on the globe.

Solar Calendar

The basis of the Chinese solar calendar is the earth's orbit around the sun.

The orbit of the earth is divided into 24 solar phases. Two solar phases together form a month. Because of the earth's elliptic orbit a month in the solar calendar lasts between 29 and 32 days. Spring equinox, summer solstice, autumn equinox and winter solstice are the culmination points of spring, summer, autumn and winter and define the center of the seasons.

The first day of the solar year is defined as the beginning of spring.

Lunar Calendar

The basis of the Chinese lunar calendar is the moon's orbit around the earth. However, it is not a pure moon calendar since the phases of the moon are taken into account, and the seasons are respected as well.

A month is the period between two new moons and lasts 29.5 days on average. There are 11 days missing to complete a year, so every 3 or 4 years a leap month is inserted to stay in sync with the seasons.

The year is usually defined to start with the second new moon after winter solstice. The first day of the lunar year is celebrated in China as New Year's Day.

Date

In China, both a solar calendar as well as a lunar calendar are in use. They differ in the definition of month and year, but day and hour are the same in both calendars.

A specific point of time is described by four celestial stem and terrestrial branch combinations for hour, day, month and year respectively.

Chinese Double Hours

A day is one rotation of the earth around its axis and lasts from midnight to midnight. A day is divided into 24 hours in the western world and into 12 double hours in China. High noon is the culmination point of the double hour from 11:00 to 13:00, and midnight is the center of the double hour from 23:00 to 01:00 of the next day.

Heavenly Stem Day / Hour Solar time	Yang Wood 甲 jia Yin Earth 己 ji	Yin Wood 乙 yi Yang Metal 庚 geng	Yang Fire 丙 bing Yin Metal 辛 xin	Yin Fire 丁 ding Yang Water 壬 ren	Yang Earth 戊 wu Yin Water 癸 gui
Rat 子 zi 00:00 – 01:00	Wood Rat 甲子 jia zi	Fire Rat 丙子 bing zi	Earth Rat 戊子 wu zi	Metal Rat 庚子 geng zi	Water Rat 壬子 ren zi
Ox 丑 chou 01:00 – 03:00	Wood Ox 乙丑 yi chou	Fire Ox 丁丑 ding chou	Earth Ox 己丑 ji chou	Metal Ox 辛丑 xin chou	Water Ox 癸丑 gui chou
Tiger 寅 yin 03:00 – 05:00	Fire Tiger 丙寅 bing yin	Earth Tiger 戊寅 wu yin	Metal Tiger 庚寅 geng yin	Water Tiger 壬寅 ren yin	Wood Tiger 甲寅 jia yin
Rabbit 卯 mao 05:00 – 07:00	Fire Rabbit 丁卯 ding mao	Earth Rabbit 己卯 ji mao	Metal Rabbit 辛卯 xin mao	Water Rabbit 癸卯 gui mao	Wood Rabbit 乙卯 yi mao
Dragon 辰 chen 07:00 – 09:00	Earth Dragon 戊辰 wu chen	Metal Dragon 庚辰 geng chen	Water Dragon 壬辰 ren chen	Wood Dragon 甲辰 jia chen	Fire Dragon 丙辰 bing chen
Snake 巳 si 09:00 – 11:00	Earth Snake 己巳 ji si	Metal Snake 辛巳 xin si	Water Snake 癸巳 gui si	Wood Snake 乙巳 yi si	Fire Snake 丁巳 ding si
Horse 午 wu 11:00 – 13:00	Metal Horse 庚午 geng wu	Water Horse 壬午 ren wu	Wood Horse 甲午 jia wu	Fire Horse 丙午 bing wu	Earth Horse 戊午 wu wu
Goat 未 wei 13:00 – 15:00	Metal Goat 辛未 xin wei	Water Goat 癸未 gui wei	Wood Goat 乙未 yi wei	Fire Goat 丁未 ding wei	Earth Goat 己未 ji wei
Monkey 申 shen 15:00 – 17:00	Water Monkey 壬申 ren shen	Wood Monkey 甲申 jia shen	Fire Monkey 丙申 bing shen	Earth Monkey 戊申 wu shen	Metal Monkey 庚申 geng shen
Rooster 酉 you 17:00 – 19:00	Water Rooster 癸酉 gui you	Wood Rooster 乙酉 yi you	Fire Rooster 丁酉 ding you	Earth Rooster 己酉 ji you	Metal Rooster 辛酉 xin you
Dog 戌 xu 19:00 – 21:00	Wood Dog 甲戌 jia xu	Fire Dog 丙戌 bing xu	Earth Dog 戊戌 wu xu	Metal Dog 庚戌 geng xu	Water Dog 壬戌 ren xu
Pig 亥 hai 21:00 – 23:00	Wood Pig 乙亥 yi hai	Fire Pig 丁亥 ding hai	Earth Pig 己亥 ji hai	Metal Pig 辛亥 xin hai	Water Pig 癸亥 gui hai
Rat 子 zi 23:00 – 00:00	Fire Rat 丙子 bing zi	Earth Rat 戊子 wu zi	Metal Rat 庚子 geng zi	Water Rat 壬子 ren zi	Wood Rat 甲子 jia zi

Time

Time is actually a rather sophisticated concept. It is not only used to give the solar time of day at your location as on a naive sundial, but also to define and communicate an exact point in time of an occurrence irrespective of your location.

Only the position of the sun was relevant historically. With the advent of rail travel and telecommunication, local time zones were introduced which defined, within their area of application, a homogeneous time. These local times easily deviate from the solar time of day by an hour or more, and daylight saving time regulations make this effect even bigger. To ease translation from one time zone to another, most time zones are nowadays defined as a fixed hourly offset from a universal world time UTC (Universal Time Coordinated).

Year, Month, Moon Phases

The Chinese calendar defines months and years based on solstices and equinoxes respectively full moon and new moon. Being caused by the movement of the celestial bodies in space such events take place at a specific point in time independent from your location on the globe. Those times are calculated and provided in Universal Time Coordinated (UTC).*

Therefore, it is necessary to convert any of the time data in the large middle column like moon phase, zodiac sign and solar phase into the local time of the time zone at your residence, taking special rules like daylight saving time into account.

Equation of Time

The Equation of Time (EOT) takes into account the astronomical effects of nutation, precession and aberration, which lead to an additional discrepancy between solar time and walltime of up to ± 18 minutes.**

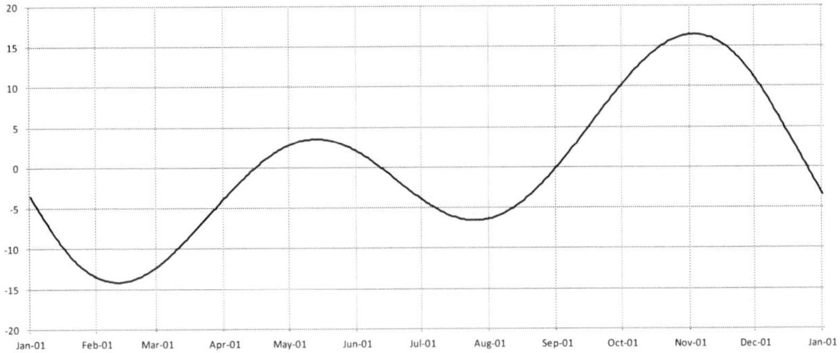

* In Chinese calendars these times are normally stated in CNST (UTC+8h) China Standard Time.

** The values of the graphic are averaged, the exact times of this year are stated at the bottom of the calendar.

Time

The moments of luck of the hours in the left column are based on the Chinese double hours which describe the altitude of the sun. The time intervals given are true solar time and must be converted into local time because differences between solar time and local walltime up to 2.5 hours within one timezone are possible.*

walltime = solar time – equation of time correction
– longitude correction to timezone + daylight saving time

The **equation of time** EOT is identical for all locations and changes by about 30 seconds per day. It is located in the footer of the left column.

The **daylight saving** *time* EDT (UTC-4h) of the eastern standard time EDT (UTC-5h) begins on the second Sunday in March and ends on the first Sunday in November. The daylight saving time CEST (UTC+2h) of the central European time CET (UTC+1h) begins on the last Sunday in March and ends on the last Sunday in October. Both can be found in the footer of the left column as well.

The **longitude correction** to time zone is caused by the difference of the longitude of the residence and the center of the time zone (75°W for EST). A longitude degree is equivalent to 4 minutes of time shift of solar time. For a specific place the longitude correction is a constant value.

Example: 20.10.2014 **12:00** solar time (sun in zenith)

CET 15°O		Santiago	Madrid	Paris	Berlin	Wien	Stockholm	Vardø
Longitude		8.53°W	3.70°W	2.35°O	13.40°O	16.37°O	18.07°O	31.11°O
Solar time		12:00	12:00	12:00	12:00	12:00	12:00	12:00
Equation of time	–	00:15	00:15	00:15	00:15	00:15	00:15	00:15
Longitude correction	–	-01:34	-01:15	-00:50	-00:06	00:05	00:12	01:05
Daylight saving time	+	1:00	1:00	1:00	1:00	1:00	1:00	1:00
Walltime CEST		**14:19**	**14:00**	**13:35**	**12:51**	**12:40**	**12:33**	**11:40**
Chinese double hour		13:19	13:00	12:35	11:51	11:40	11:33	10:40
11:00 – 13:00		- 15:19	-15:00	-14:35	- 13:51	- 13:40	- 13:33	- 12:40

EST 75°W		Thunder Bay	Louisville	Washington	New York	Boston	Gaspé
Longitude		89.25°W	85.76°W	77.04°W	74.01°W	71.06°W	64.49°W
Solar time		12:00	12:00	12:00	12:00	12:00	12:00
Equation of time	–	00:15	00:15	00:15	00:15	00:15	00:15
Longitude correction	–	-00:57	-00:43	-00:08	00:04	00:16	00:42
Daylight saving time	+	1:00	1:00	1:00	1:00	1:00	1:00
Walltime EDT		**13:42**	**13:28**	**12:53**	**12:41**	**12:29**	**12:03**
Chinese double hour		12:42	12:28	11:53	11:41	11:29	11:03
11:00 – 13:00		- 14:42	- 14:28	- 13:53	- 13:41	- 13:29	- 13:03

With the solar time calculator you can look up the equation of time and the longitude effect and convert solar time to local time and vice versa.

www.wangnick.com/software_timecalculator.htm

* The exact beginning of the double hours at your place of residence and your personal Moments of Luck are given in your individually calculated calendar (page 207).

Moments of Luck

Each day has a specific quality. It is based on the interaction of the energies of day, month and year. The general **quality of a day** is classified in five categories from ☆☆ very difficult and ☆ difficult over ★ average, ★★ good up to ★★★ excellent. The icons are located directly beneath the date. A flash ϟ denotes a day or hour with explosive energy. Take precautions and do not use such times for important undertakings.

The **Moments of Luck of the day** are specific energies are conducive or obstructive to special activities. There are icons for auspicious endeavors such as ♥♥ love, ♥ communication, ✈ travel, € money, ⏻ start, ✹ support and crossed symbols ♥♥ ♥ ✈ ⏻ € ✹ for transactions to avoid. They are listed on the top of each day on the right underneath the date.

The Moments of Luck of the day are refined by the **Moments of Luck of the hour**. They are depicted on the left border of each day. The crucial factor is the starting time of the activity. The energy of the day is stronger than the hour's energy. The hour supports the day but cannot compensate the day's outcome.

In the Chinese calendar time is specified using double hours. Their duration is indicated in the left column of the day. The double hours reflect the qi of the sun and the position of the sun as it can be read on a sundial. Due to timezone and daylight saving time this solar time can differ from the walltime by more than 1.5 hours in Germany and up to 2.5 hours in the scope of the central European time. This moves a date very quickly from one double hour into the next. The precise procedure for time adjustment is explained in the section about time on page 147.

In this calendar the individual energy of a person is incorporated only by the animal sign and the nayin of the birth year. Based on the Chinese horoscope of a person, his individual moments of luck of the day and the hour can be calculated.*

You will notice that hour statements may contradict the day. Then take heed of the following principles:

- Personal is more important than general.
- Avoid explosive energy.
- Avoid negative.
- The day is more important than the hour.

In front of the calendar you find an overview of your good dates for fast access.

* The exact beginning of the double hours at your place of residence and your personal Moments of Luck are given in your individually calculated calendar (page 207).

Moments of Luck

It is written in the bible*:

„To every thing there is a season,
and a time to every purpose under the heaven."

In Asia, the selection of an appropriate date for the start of an endeavor is of very high significance. The more significant the event, the more important the selection of a good moment to begin. The duration of the undertaking is irrelevant, the good start is most important.

Approach to Date Selection

1. Decide about the main focus of the activity:
   business opening ⏻ , negotiation ♥ , contract signing € , marriage ♥♥ .
   Additional support ✹ is preferable.
2. Search for a **day** with an appropriate symbol.
3. The day must not clash with *your personal Chinese animal sign* – extremely important (page 175).
4. The day may not have a flash ⚡ – very important.
5. The day should have at least one star ★ – important.
6. The day should support *your personal Nayin* – important (page 160).
7. Search for a suitable **hour**** within the day with appropriate or supporting positive icons.
8. The hour must not must not clash with *your personal Chinese animal sign* – very important (page 175).
9. The hour should not have a flash ⚡ – important.
10. Check the officer on duty.
11. Does the I Ching of the day fit?
12. Do moon phase, moon zodiac sign and lunar mansion support the project?

Take the list above as priority list. Exclude the days with a flash and look for a day that suits you *personally* (Point 3, 6, 9) with as much appropriate positive symbols as possible. Use the starting time for fine-tuning.

Example: You plan to go on a journey. Look for a day with ✈ and without ⚡. If the journey has to take place on a fixed date, place the departure in an hour without ✈̸ or ⚡ and with ✈ or ✹ if possible or check in at this time.

Optimal dates are rare and difficult to find, in particular if you have a restricted period (must start in May) or limitations on weekdays (no weekends) or day times (only in the morning).

* The Bible, Old Testament, Ecclesiastes Salomo, chapter 3

** Time adjustment is required. Refer to the annotations concerning time (page 147).

Western Moon Calendar

The moon influences life on earth. It provokes the tide and influences growth and health of plants. Whilst the sun takes a year to go once through the zodiac, the moon needs 27.3 days for this journey. The astronomical constellations occupy different sized regions of the sky. The astrological zodiac describes, similar to the Chinese terrestrial branches, angular relations and therefore equally sized parts of the orbit. Constellations and zodiac had been congruent in Babylonian times, but have diverged to two days of difference by now. This is the reason for different data in western moon calendars. This calendar calculates the position of the moon according to the astrological zodiac. You can find the progression of the moon phase from the Chinese moon calendar on the top of the calendar page. Up to the 14th day the moon is waxing, afterwards it is waning.

Moon Phases

☽	Waxing Moon	expanding, water ascends, earth exhales sowing or planting of foliage, flower and fruit plants start herbal essences
○	Full Moon	full of tension no sowing or planting harvest herbs for magic and medicine
☾	Waning Moon	contracting, water declines, earth inhales sowing or planting of root plants weed, cut
●	New Moon	calming, purifying no sowing or planting harvest roots for magic and medicine

Moon in Zodiac Signs

♑	Capricorn	root	ascending moon	sowing
♒	Aquarius	flower	ascending moon	sowing
♓	Pisces	foliage	ascending moon	sowing
♈	Aries	fruit	ascending moon	sowing
♉	Taurus	root	ascending moon	sowing
♊	Gemini	flower	ascending moon	sowing
♋	Cancer	foliage	descending moon	harvest
♌	Leo	fruit	descending moon	harvest
♍	Virgo	root	descending moon	harvest
♎	Libra	flower	descending moon	harvest
♏	Scorpio	foliage	descending moon	harvest
♐	Sagittarius	fruit	descending moon	harvest

Officers

The system of the twelve officers on duty is based on the energetic compatibility of the terrestrial branches of day and month. An officer on duty stands for a specific sort of qi on this day. Because of differences in assessments in the literature I recommend cautious and experimental use. In the calendar auspicious officers are printed in black and unfavorable officers are shown in grey. ⮝ introduces auspicious activities, ⮟ is followed by actions which should be avoided.

Balance auspicious
⮝ marriage, change of residence, meditation, renovation
⮟ gardening, digging a pond

Closing unfavorable
⮝ burial, erecting a memorial stone
⮟ most activities

Completion auspicious
⮝ contract negotiations, marriage, travel, earth moving
⮟ accusations, gossip

Danger unfavourable
⮝
⮟ difficulties, danger of accidents

Destruction unfavorable
⮝ lawsuits, divorce
⮟ conflicts

Determination auspicious
⮝ all activities, marriage, gardening, earth moving
⮟ accusations

Establishment auspicious
⮝ beginning new ventures, travel, trade
⮟ opening a store, earth moving, construction

Fulfillment auspicious
⮝ festivities, marriage, travel, change of residence
⮟ gardening

Harvest auspicious
⮝ marriage, trade, earth moving, starting studies, activity
⮟ travel, burial, acupuncture

Opening auspicious
⮝ business contracts, crafts, travel, wedding arrangement
⮟ burial

Removal unfavorable
⮝ cleaning, hygiene, health, sport
⮟ business transactions, gatherings, marriage, travel, digging a pond

Rigidity unfavorable
⮝ routine work, digging a pond, gardening, marriage, inquiries
⮟ travel, change of residence, opening a store

Lunar Mansions

Originally, the lunar mansions were used to describe the position of the moon on the ecliptic. Each of the 28 lunar mansions matches a constellation. The astronomical constellations occupy different sized regions of the firmament. Therefore, the time the moon spends in one constellation differs from some hours to several days. Lunar mansions were used for weather forecasts in agriculture and for fortune telling.

Over the years this system got significantly simplified, and nowadays each day has its own lunar mansion, which is independent of the real position of the moon. Lunar mansions are very popular in Asia and often used to select auspicious days for extraordinary events, but I recommend cautious and experimental use. In the calendar, auspicious lunar mansions are printed in black and unfavorable lunar mansions are shown in grey. ⮝ introduces auspicious activities, ⮟ is followed by actions which should be avoided.

Astride unfavorable
⮟ construction, renovation, earth-moving, burial, project kick-off, contracts

Base unfavorable
⮝ clarification
⮟ construction, marriage, burial

Basket auspicious
⮝ construction, renovation, door opening, marriage, burial, project kick-off

Beak unfavorable
⮟ construction, renovation, burial

Bowauspicious
⮝ construction, renovation, marriage, burial, water features

Carriage auspicious
⮝ construction, renovation, gardening, marriage, burial, commerce

Dipper auspicious
⮝ construction, renovation, water features, project kick-off, marriage, earth-moving, burial

Ghosts unfavorable
⮝ burial
⮟ construction, renovation, door opening, marriage

Heart unfavorable
⮟ construction, renovation, marriage, burial

Horn auspicious
⮝ construction, renovation, marriage, project kick-off, land purchase, investments
⮟ burial, project end

House auspicious
⮝ construction, renovation, project kick-off, marriage, burial

Lunar Mansions

Maiden unfavorable
- ⮟ construction, renovation, marriage, burial

Neck unfavorable
- ⮟ construction, marriage, burial, project kick-off

Net auspicious
- ⮝ construction, renovation, marriage, burial

Orion (in-)auspicious
- ⮝ construction, renovation, water features, project kick-off
- ⮟ marriage, burial, project end

Ox unfavorable
- ⮟ construction, renovation, marriage, project kick-off, contracts

Pleiades unfavorable
- ⮟ construction, renovation, water features, marriage, burial, project kick-off, earth-moving

Roof unfavorable
- ⮟ construction, renovation, burial, store opening, travel

Room auspicious
- ⮝ construction, renovation, water features, marriage, burial, project kick-off

Rope auspicious
- ⮝ marriage, construction, renovation, door opening, water features, earth moving, gatherings

Star unfavorable
- ⮝ construction, renovation
- ⮟ marriage, burial, water features

Stomach auspicious
- ⮝ investment, construction, renovation, marriage, burial, earth moving

Tail auspicious
- ⮝ construction, renovation, water features, marriage, career, project kick-off, burial

Void unfavorable
- ⮟ construction, renovation, water features, earth-moving, marriage, family gathering

Wall auspicious
- ⮝ construction, renovation, door opening, water features, earth-moving, marriage, burial, project kick-off

Well (in-)auspicious
- ⮝ examination, construction, renovation, door opening, water features, gardening
- ⮟ burial, tranquility

Willow unfavorable
- ⮟ construction, renovation, marriage, burial, project kick-off

Wings unfavorable
- ⮟ travel, construction, renovation, marriage, burial

I Ching

The famous Chinese philosopher Lao Tse wrote in his book Tao Te King: "The knowledge of the ancient beginnings is the essence of the future path."

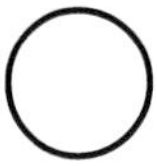

The beginning of all things is the basic energy Wuji. Its symbol is a circle. A circle is at the same time empty and full. It contains everything.

The circle, an unfertilized egg, is transformed by a point, a single sperm. This gives birth to Yin and Yang, the genesis of both fundamental forces of the universe. With their effect on each other, all development starts.

Yin and Yang depend on each other. They penetrate each other and move in equilibrium. Where Yang diminishes, Yin grows. But where Yang is at its greatest, a spark of Yin is still present. This is how the Taiji is created. The interaction of Yin and Yang gives rise to the entire reality. Creativity (Yang) and Receptivity (Yin) generate the "Ten-Thousand Things".

Yang, the father of heaven, creativity, energy, is represented as **+** or a straight line. Yin, the mother of earth, receptivity, matter, is represented as **–** or an interrupted line.

A trigram is a combination of Yin and Yang. It consists of three lines of either Yin or Yang, describing the trinity of heaven, man and earth. The eight Trigrams are ☰ Qian Heaven and ☷ Kun Earth, ☲ Li Fire and ☵ Kan Water, ☳ Zhen Thunder and ☴ Xun Wind, ☶ Gen Mountain and ☱ Dui Lake.

The encounter of two trigrams within a hexagram establishes the relation between heaven (the upper trigram) and earth (the lower trigram). Every hexagram represents a unique aspect of the world.

The combination of Yin and Yang and their variants are explained in the "Book of Changes"*, I Ching or Yijing, which establishes a prophecy for every hexagram. These prophecies are not immutuable predictions but indications of opportunities providing motivation and admonition. Everything is in flux, nothing remains the same. This knowledge is the foundation of the I Ching.

* ie, Richard Wilhelm: I CHING or book of changes, Arkana, 1989

Five Elements

The Five Elements

The five elements, also known as energies or phases of change, describe five different types of energy. **Wood** is rising energy. **Fire** stands for exploding and expanding energy in all directions. **Earth** is energy coming down to earth. **Metal** is contracting energy. **Water** is shapeless and floating energy.

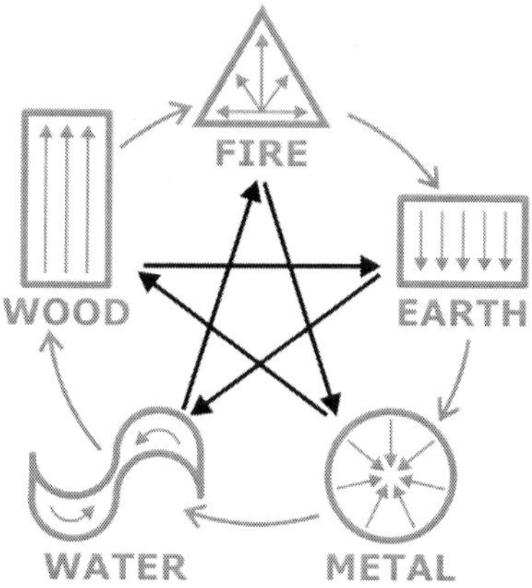

The five energies transform naturally one into the other. Rising, extending, descending, contracting and disintegrating and new ascending form a cycle, the productive cycle (→).

Wood → Fire → Earth → Metal → Water → Wood

In the controlling cycle (➔) the five elements control each other intensity and influence.

Wood ➔ Earth ➔ Water ➔ Fire ➔ Metal ➔ Wood

However, you have to take the strength of the elements into account. Too much production weakens the producer, and too much control can destroy.

Heavenly Stems and Earthly Branches

Each element has specific characteristics.

	Wood	Fire	Earth	Metal	Water
Energy	rising	exploding	descending	contracting	floating
Form	tall rectangle	spiky triangle	flat square	round sphere	undulated polygon
Color	green turquoise	red orange	yellow brown	white grey silver gold	blue black
Material	wood paper plants	fire light	pottery stone ceramics	metal	water glass plastics
Taste	sour	bitter	sweet	spicy	salty
Organ	liver eyes	heart tongue	spleen mouth	lungs nose	kidneys ears
Attitude	creativity	joy	stability	concentration	action

An element can be activated by decorating a room with objects or colors. But you can also utilize your attitude or your clothing. Bed-linen is best at night. By day, underwear is perfect because it is in direct contact with your skin and thus provides invisible support.

Heavenly Stems

A heavenly stem represents the energy of heaven. It is a combination of Yin or Yang and an element Wood, Fire, Earth, Metal or Water.

甲	jia	Yang	Wood	East
乙	yi	Yin	Wood	East
丙	bing	Yang	Fire	South
丁	ding	Yin	Fire	South
戊	wu	Yang	Earth	Center
己	ji	Yin	Earth	Center
庚	geng	Yang	Metal	West
辛	xin	Yin	Metal	West
壬	ren	Yang	Water	North
癸	gui	Yin	Water	North

Heavenly Stems and Earthly Branches

Earthly Branches

An earthly branch represents the energy of the earth. It is also a combination of Yin or Yang, and an element Wood, Fire, Earth, Metal or Water. The Earth finishes each season.

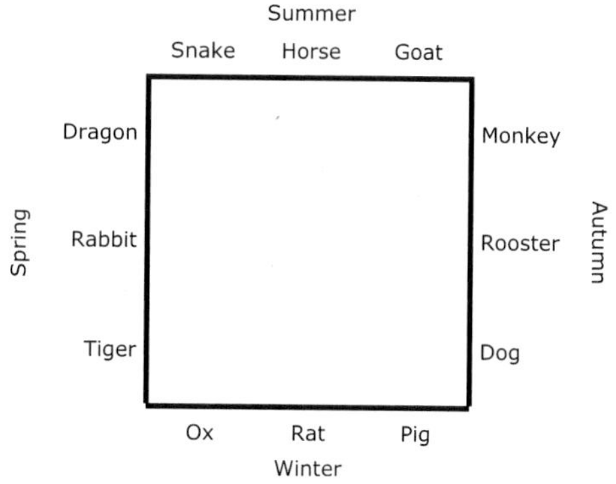

子	zi	Yang	Water	Rat	23:00– 1:00	December
丑	chou	Yin	Earth$_{Water}$	Ox	1:00– 3:00	January
寅	yin	Yang	Wood	Tiger	3:00– 5:00	February
卯	mao	Yin	Wood	Rabbit	5:00– 7:00	Marh
辰	chen	Yang	Earth$_{Wood}$	Dragon	7:00– 9:00	April
巳	si	Yin	Fire	Snake	9:00–11:00	May
午	wu	Yang	Fire	Horse	11:00–13:00	June
未	wei	Yin	Earth$_{Fire}$	Goat	13:00–15:00	July
申	shen	Yang	Metal	Monkey	15:00–17:00	August
酉	you	Yin	Metal	Rooster	17:00–19:00	September
戌	xu	Yang	Earth$_{Metal}$	Dog	19:00–21:00	October
亥	hai	Yin	Water	Pig	21:00–23:00	November

Heavenly Stem and Earthly Branch Combination

In China, time is seen as a coincidence of heaven's and earth's energy, represented by a celestial stem and an terrestrial branch. Year, month, day and time are each represented by an own stem-branch combination and form the four pillars of a date. In the calendar, the day pillar is printed right beside the date, year and month pillars are shown in the header and footer.

甲子 jia zi Wood Yang Water Wood Rat

denote the same stem-branch combination. There are 60 different combinations because yang stems combine only with yang branches and yin stems with yin branches.

Nayin - Hidden Tones

Nayin means contained or hidden tone. Year, month, day and hour are each described by a combination of a heavenly stem and an earthly branch. The simultaneous vibration of heaven's and earth's qi generates a unique tone, the nayin.

There are thirty different hidden tones. Each of them has a basic tune based on the five elements.

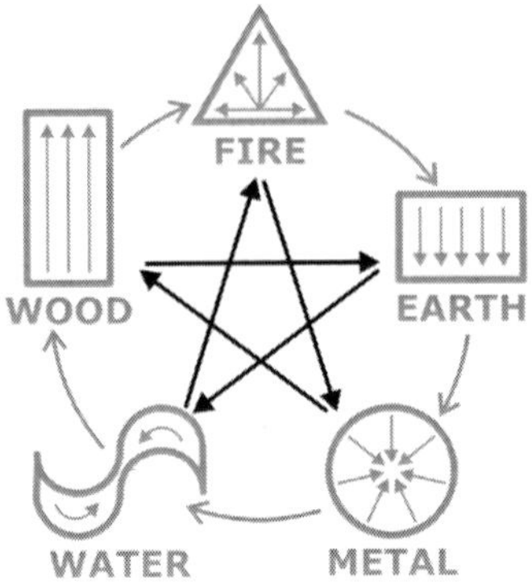

A tune enhances the following tune harmonically ≈, if both tunes are equal or if a grey → or black ➔ arrow starts with the first tune and points to the second tune. Otherwise it sounds dissonant ≠.

The nayin offer a harmonic variant to judge a date. The focus is the human being and its personal nayin. It is desirable that the day supports the person.

Your personal nayin depends on your year of birth. You can look it up on page 160 and complete the chart below.

Your personal nayin is ....

From the perspective of nayin, the tone of the day means to you personally:

....	*Day* = *Person*	....	The day supports you.
....	*Day* → *Person*	....	The day strengthens you.
....	*Day* ➔ *Person*	....	The day controls you and provides structure.
....	*Person* ➔ *Day*	....	You control the day and weaken yourself.
....	*Person* → *Day*	....	You strengthen the day and exhaust yourself.

Nayin

The nayin offer a highly sophisticated possibility to describe the energy of a day. Therefore, the nayin of the month and year are included. Preferable is a sequence of yearly, monthly and daily notes that harmonically enhance the vibration of your personal note.

yearly nayin ≈ monthly nayin ≈ daily nayin ≈ personal nayin

In the calendar, the nayin is shown in italic on the right side of the stem-branch combination of the day, and at the bottom of the page for month and year.

Begin	**Year**		**Month**		**Day**		**Good for Persons**		
2021-12-06	*Earth*	≈	*Earth*	≈	*Earth*	≈	*Earth*	*Metal*	*Water*
					Metal	≈	*Metal*	*Water*	*Wood*
					Water	≈	*Water*	*Wood*	*Fire*
2022-02-03	*Metal*	≈	*Metal*	≈	*Metal*	≈	*Metal*	*Water*	*Wood*
					Water	≈	*Water*	*Wood*	*Fire*
					Wood	≈	*Wood*	*Fire*	*Earth*
2022-04-04	*Metal*	≠	*Fire*	≈	*Fire*	≈	*Fire*	*Earth*	*Metal*
					Earth	≈	*Earth*	*Metal*	*Water*
					Metal	≈	*Metal*	*Water*	*Wood*
2022-06-05	*Metal*	≈	*Water*	≈	*Water*	≈	*Water*	*Wood*	*Fire*
					Wood	≈	*Wood*	*Fire*	*Earth*
					Fire	≈	*Fire*	*Earth*	*Metal*
2022-08-07	*Metal*	≠	*Earth*	≈	*Earth*	≈	*Earth*	*Metal*	*Water*
					Metal	≈	*Metal*	*Water*	*Wood*
					Water	≈	*Water*	*Wood*	*Fire*
2022-10-08	*Metal*	≈	*Metal*	≈	*Metal*	≈	*Metal*	*Water*	*Wood*
					Water	≈	*Water*	*Wood*	*Fire*
					Wood	≈	*Wood*	*Fire*	*Earth*
2022-12-07	*Metal*	≈	*Wood*	≈	*Wood*	≈	*Wood*	*Fire*	*Earth*
					Fire	≈	*Fire*	*Earth*	*Metal*
					Earth	≈	*Earth*	*Metal*	*Water*
2023-02-04	*Metal*	≈	*Water*	≈	*Water*	≈	*Water*	*Wood*	*Fire*
					Wood	≈	*Wood*	*Fire*	*Earth*
					Fire	≈	*Fire*	*Earth*	*Metal*

Ming Gua and Nayin Table

Year	Begin Lunar/Solar	Male	Female	Nayin
1920 Metal Monkey	20.02. 05.02. 02:26	8	7	Wood
1921 Metal Rooster	08.02. 04.02. 08:20	7	8	Wood
1922 Water Dog	28.01. 04.02. 14:06	6	9	Water
1923 Water Pig	16.02. 04.02. 20:00	2	1	Water
1924 Wood Rat	05.02. 05.02. 01:50	4	2	Metal
1925 Wood Ox	24.01. 04.02. 07:37	3	3	Metal
1926 Fire Tiger	13.02. 04.02. 13:38	2	4	Fire
1927 Fire Rabbit	02.02. 04.02. 19:30	1	8	Fire
1928 Earth Dragon	23.01. 05.02. 01:16	9	6	Wood
1929 Earth Snake	10.02. 04.02. 07:09	8	7	Wood
1930 Metal Horse	30.01. 04.02. 12:51	7	8	Earth
1931 Metal Goat	17.02. 04.02. 18:41	6	9	Earth
1932 Water Monkey	06.02. 05.02. 00:29	2	1	Metal
1933 Water Rooster	26.01. 04.02. 06:09	4	2	Metal
1934 Wood Dog	14.02. 04.02. 12:04	3	3	Fire
1935 Wood Pig	04.02. 04.02. 17:49	2	4	Fire
1936 Fire Rat	24.01. 04.02. 23:29	1	8	Water
1937 Fire Ox	11.02. 04.02. 05:26	9	6	Water
1938 Earth Tiger	31.01. 04.02. 11:15	8	7	Earth
1939 Earth Rabbit	19.02. 04.02. 17:10	7	8	Earth
1940 Metal Dragon	08.02. 04.02. 23:08	6	9	Metal
1941 Metal Snake	27.01. 04.02. 04:50	2	1	Metal
1942 Water Horse	15.02. 04.02. 10:49	4	2	Wood
1943 Water Goat	05.02. 04.02. 16:40	3	3	Wood
1944 Wood Monkey	25.01. 04.02. 22:23	2	4	Water
1945 Wood Rooster	13.02. 04.02. 04:19	1	8	Water
1946 Fire Dog	02.02. 04.02. 10:04	9	6	Earth
1947 Fire Pig	22.01. 04.02. 15:50	8	7	Earth
1948 Earth Rat	10.02. 04.02. 21:42	7	8	Fire
1949 Earth Ox	29.01. 04.02. 03:23	6	9	Fire
1950 Metal Tiger	17.02. 04.02. 09:21	2	1	Wood
1951 Metal Rabbit	06.02. 04.02. 15:13	4	2	Wood
1952 Water Dragon	27.01. 04.02. 20:53	3	3	Water
1953 Water Snake	14.02. 04.02. 02:46	2	4	Water
1954 Wood Horse	03.02. 04.02. 08:31	1	8	Metal
1955 Wood Goat	24.01. 04.02. 14:18	9	6	Metal

Year	Begin Lunar/Solar	Male	Female	Nayin
1956 Fire Monkey	12.02. 04.02. 20:12	8	7	Fire
1957 Fire Rooster	31.01. 04.02. 01:55	7	8	Fire
1958 Earth Dog	18.02. 04.02. 07:49	6	9	Wood
1959 Earth Pig	08.02. 04.02. 13:42	2	1	Wood
1960 Metal Rat	28.01. 04.02. 19:23	4	2	Earth
1961 Metal Ox	15.02. 04.02. 01:23	3	3	Earth
1962 Water Tiger	05.02. 04.02. 07:17	2	4	Metal
1963 Water Rabbit	25.01. 04.02. 13:08	1	8	Metal
1964 Wood Dragon	13.02. 04.02. 19:05	9	6	Fire
1965 Wood Snake	02.02. 04.02. 00:46	8	7	Fire
1966 Fire Horse	21.01. 04.02. 06:38	7	8	Water
1967 Fire Goat	09.02. 04.02. 12:31	6	9	Water
1968 Earth Monkey	30.01. 04.02. 18:08	2	1	Earth
1969 Earth Rooster	17.02. 03.02. 23:59	4	2	Earth
1970 Metal Dog	06.02. 04.02. 05:46	3	3	Metal
1971 Metal Pig	27.01. 04.02. 11:26	2	4	Metal
1972 Water Rat	15.02. 04.02. 17:20	1	8	Wood
1973 Water Ox	03.02. 03.02. 23:04	9	6	Wood
1974 Wood Tiger	23.01. 04.02. 05:00	8	7	Water
1975 Wood Rabbit	11.02. 04.02. 10:59	7	8	Water
1976 Fire Dragon	31.01. 04.02. 16:40	6	9	Earth
1977 Fire Snake	18.02. 03.02. 22:34	2	1	Earth
1978 Earth Horse	07.02. 04.02. 04:27	4	2	Fire
1979 Earth Goat	28.01. 04.02. 10:13	3	3	Fire
1980 Metal Monkey	16.02. 04.02. 16:10	2	4	Wood
1981 Metal Rooster	05.02. 03.02. 21:56	1	8	Wood
1982 Water Dog	25.01. 04.02. 03:46	9	6	Water
1983 Water Pig	13.02. 04.02. 09:40	8	7	Water
1984 Wood Rat	02.02. 04.02. 15:19	7	8	Metal
1985 Wood Ox	20.02. 03.02. 21:12	6	9	Metal
1986 Fire Tiger	09.02. 04.02. 03:08	2	1	Fire
1987 Fire Rabbit	29.01. 04.02. 08:52	4	2	Fire
1988 Earth Dragon	17.02. 04.02. 14:43	3	3	Wood
1989 Earth Snake	06.02. 03.02. 20:28	2	4	Wood
1990 Metal Horse	27.01. 04.02. 02:14	1	8	Earth
1991 Metal Goat	15.02. 04.02. 08:09	9	6	Earth

Year	Begin Lunar/Solar	Male	Female	Nayin
1992 Water Monkey	04.02. 04.02. 13:49	8	7	Metal
1993 Water Rooster	23.01. 03.02. 19:38	7	8	Metal
1994 Wood Dog	10.02. 04.02. 01:31	6	9	Fire
1995 Wood Pig	31.01. 04.02. 07:13	2	1	Fire
1996 Fire Rat	19.02. 04.02. 13:08	4	2	Water
1997 Fire Ox	07.02. 03.02. 19:02	3	3	Water
1998 Earth Tiger	28.01. 04.02. 00:57	2	4	Earth
1999 Earth Rabbit	16.02. 04.02. 06:58	1	8	Earth
2000 Metal Dragon	05.02. 04.02. 12:41	9	6	Metal
2001 Metal Snake	24.01. 03.02. 18:29	8	7	Metal
2002 Water Horse	12.02. 04.02. 00:25	7	8	Wood
2003 Water Goat	01.02. 04.02. 06:06	6	9	Wood
2004 Wood Monkey	22.01. 04.02. 11:57	2	1	Water
2005 Wood Rooster	09.02. 03.02. 17:44	4	2	Water
2006 Fire Dog	29.01. 03.02. 23:28	3	3	Earth
2007 Fire Pig	18.02. 04.02. 05:19	2	4	Earth
2008 Earth Rat	07.02. 04.02. 11:01	1	8	Fire
2009 Earth Ox	26.01. 03.02. 16:50	9	6	Fire
2010 Metal Tiger	14.02. 03.02. 22:48	8	7	Wood
2011 Metal Rabbit	03.02. 04.02. 04:34	7	8	Wood
2012 Water Dragon	23.01. 04.02. 10:23	6	9	Water
2013 Water Snake	10.02. 03.02. 16:14	2	1	Water
2014 Wood Horse	31.01. 03.02. 22:04	4	2	Metal
2015 Wood Goat	19.02. 04.02. 03:59	3	3	Metal
2016 Fire Monkey	08.02. 04.02. 09:47	2	4	Fire
2017 Fire Rooster	28.01. 03.02. 15:35	1	8	Fire
2018 Earth Dog	16.02. 03.02. 21:29	9	6	Wood
2019 Earth Pig	05.02. 04.02. 03:15	8	7	Wood
2020 Metal Rat	25.01. 04.02. 09:04	7	8	Earth
2021 Metal Ox	12.02. 03.02. 14:59	6	9	Earth
2022 Water Tiger	01.02. 03.02.20:51	2	1	Metal
2023 Water Rabbit	22.01. 04.02. 02:43	4	2	Metal
2024 Wood Dragon	10.02. 04.02. 08:28	3	3	Fire
2025 Wood Snake	29.01. 03.02. 14:11	2	4	Fire
2026 Fire Horse	17.02. 03.02. 20:03	1	8	Water
2027 Fire Goat	06.02. 04.02. 01:47	9	6	Water

Time data is given in Universal Time Coordinated (UTC). Adaptation is required.
Example: 15:50 UTC correlates to 16:50 CET (UTC+1) Central European Time, 23:50 CNST (UTC+8) China Standard Time, 10:50 EST (UTC-5) Eastern Standard Time, 07:50 PST (UTC-8) Pacific Standard Time.

Ming Gua – Areas of Life

Gua means trigram. Each person has a personal trigram called ming gua. It is derived from the Chinese year of birth and the sex. Each trigram is associated with a number, the gua number. You can find your personal ming gua number in the table of gua numbers.

The trigrams and numbers are divided into two groups, the east group, consisting of ☵ Kan 1, ☳ Zhen 3, ☴ Xun 4 and ☲ Li 9, and the west group consisting of ☷ Kun 2, ☰ Qian 6, ☱ Dui 7 and ☶ Gen 8.

The compass directions associated to the east group, North, East, Southeast and South are recommended for east group members and difficult for west group individuals. Southwest, West, Northwest und Northeast are the compass directions of the west group trigrams. These directions are inauspicious for east group members and auspicious for persons with a west group ming gua.

East group

Gua	Vitality	Health	Harmony	Clarity	Adversity	Annoyance	Sickness	Disaster
1	Southeast	East	South	North	West	Northeast	Northwest	Southwest
3	South	North	Southeast	East	Southwest	Northwest	Northeast	West
4	North	South	East	South East	Northwest	Southwest	West	Northeast
9	East	Southeast	North	South	Northeast	West	Southwest	Northwest

West group

Gua	Vitality	Health	Harmony	Clarity	Adversity	Annoyance	Sickness	Disaster
2	Northeast	West	Northwest	Southwest	East	Southeast	South	North
6	West	Northeast	Southwest	Northwest	Southeast	East	North	South
7	Northwest	Southwest	Northeast	West	North	South	Southeast	East
8	Southwest	Northwest	West	Northeast	South	North	East	Southeast

Each compass direction has a specific effect on each ming gua. This should be taken into consideration when positioning bed and desk.

Vitality	★★★★	authority, strength, wealth
Health	★★★	good health, support
Harmony	★★	good relationships, longevity
Clarity	★	stability, calm, ease
Adversity	ϟ	mishaps, obstacles
Annoyance	ϟϟ	setbacks, gossip, resistance
Sickness	ϟϟϟ	accidents, betrayal, lawsuits
Disaster	ϟϟϟϟ	catastrophe, life threatening situations

Ming Gua – 24 Mountains

Within the compass direction of a trigram, there are variations in quality and intensity for each ming gua.

When subdividing the 8 trigrams into 24 mountains, the pure energy appears only in the second middle sector of each trigram. In the first and third sector the basic energy is amplified ★☆ ϟ↯, diminished ★☆ ϟ↯ or interfered ★↯ ϟ☆.

Direction \ Person		East group				West group			
		☵ 1	☳ 3	☴ 4	☲ 9	☷ 2	☰ 6	☱ 7	☶ 8
☵ Kan	N1	★☆	★★★☆	★★★☆	★☆	ϟϟϟ↯	ϟϟϟ↯	ϟ↯	ϟ↯
	N2	★	★★★	★★★★	★★	ϟϟϟϟ	ϟϟϟ	ϟ	ϟϟ
	N3	★	★★★	★★★★	★★	ϟϟϟϟ	ϟϟϟ	ϟ	ϟϟ
☶ Gen	NE1	ϟ↯	ϟϟϟ↯	ϟϟϟ↯	ϟ↯	★★★☆	★★★☆	★☆	★☆
	NE2	ϟϟ	ϟϟϟ	ϟϟϟϟ	ϟ	★★★★	★★★	★★	★
	NE3	ϟϟ☆☆	ϟϟϟ☆☆☆☆	ϟϟϟϟ☆☆☆	ϟ☆	★★★★↯↯↯	★★★↯↯↯↯	★★↯↯	★↯
☳ Zhen	E1	★★★↯↯↯	★↯↯	★★↯	★★★★↯↯↯↯	ϟ☆☆	ϟϟ☆	ϟϟϟϟ☆☆☆☆	ϟϟϟ☆☆☆
	E2	★★★	★	★★	★★★★	ϟ	ϟϟ	ϟϟϟϟ	ϟϟϟ
	E3	★★★↯↯↯↯	★↯	★★↯↯	★★★★↯↯↯	ϟ☆	ϟϟ☆☆	ϟϟϟϟ☆☆☆	ϟϟϟ☆☆☆☆
☴ Xun	SE1	★☆☆☆	★★☆	★☆☆☆	★★☆	ϟϟ↯↯	ϟ↯↯	ϟ↯↯	ϟϟ↯↯
	SE2	★★★★	★★	★	★★★	ϟϟ	ϟ	ϟϟϟ	ϟϟϟϟ
	SE3	★★★★↯	★★↯↯↯↯	★↯↯↯	★★★↯↯	ϟϟ☆☆☆	ϟ☆☆☆☆	ϟϟϟ☆	ϟϟϟϟ☆☆
☲ Li	S1	★★↯↯	★★★★↯↯↯	★★★↯↯↯↯	★↯	ϟϟϟ☆☆☆☆	ϟϟϟϟ☆☆☆	ϟϟ☆☆	ϟ☆
	S2	★★	★★★★	★★★	★	ϟϟϟ	ϟϟϟϟ	ϟϟ	ϟ
	S3	★★↯	★★★★↯↯↯↯	★★★↯↯	★↯↯	ϟϟϟ☆☆☆	ϟϟϟϟ☆☆☆☆	ϟϟ☆	ϟ☆☆
☷ Kun	SW1	ϟϟϟϟ☆☆☆	ϟ☆	ϟϟ☆☆	ϟϟϟ☆☆☆☆	★↯	★★↯↯	★★★↯↯↯	★★★★↯↯↯
	SW2	ϟϟϟϟ	ϟ	ϟϟ	ϟϟϟ	★	★★	★★★	★★★★
	SW3	ϟϟϟϟ☆	ϟ☆☆☆	ϟϟ☆☆☆☆	ϟϟϟ☆☆	★↯↯↯	★★↯↯↯	★★★↯	★★★★↯↯
☱ Dui	W1	ϟ☆☆☆	ϟϟϟϟ☆	ϟϟϟ☆☆	ϟϟ☆☆☆☆	★★★↯	★★★★↯↯	★↯↯↯	★★↯↯↯
	W2	ϟ	ϟϟϟϟ	ϟϟϟ	ϟϟ	★★★	★★★★	★	★★
	W3	ϟ☆☆☆☆	ϟϟϟϟ☆☆	ϟϟϟ☆	ϟϟ☆☆☆	★★★↯↯	★★★★↯	★↯↯	★★↯↯↯↯
☰ Qian	NW1	ϟϟϟ☆☆	ϟϟ☆☆☆☆	ϟ☆☆☆	ϟϟϟϟ☆	★★↯↯↯	★↯↯↯↯	★★★★↯↯	★★★↯
	NW2	ϟϟϟ	ϟϟ	ϟ	ϟϟϟϟ	★★	★	★★★★	★★★
	NW3	ϟϟϟ☆☆☆	ϟϟ☆	ϟ☆☆	ϟϟϟϟ☆☆☆☆	★★↯	★↯↯	★★★★↯↯↯↯	★★★↯↯↯

Ming Gua – Luo Shu

Summary of the compass directions and their significance for each ming gua

SE	157.5°	S	202.5°	SW
112.5°	☴ Xun **1** – Vitality **3** – Harmony **4** – Clarity **9** – Health **2** – Annoyance **6** – Adversity **7** – Sickness **8** – Disaster	☲ Li **1** – Harmony **3** – Vitality **4** – Health **9** – Clarity **2** – Sickness **6** – Disaster **7** – Annoyance **8** – Adversity	☷ Kun **1** – Disaster **3** – Adversity **4** – Annoyance **9** – Sickness **2** – Clarity **6** – Harmony **7** – Health **8** – Vitality	247.5°
E	☳ Zhen **1** – Health **3** – Clarity **4** – Harmony **9** – Vitality **2** – Adversity **6** – Annoyance **7** – Disaster **8** – Sickness	☯	☱ Dui **1** – Adversity **3** – Disaster **4** – Sickness **9** – Annoyance **2** – Health **6** – Vitality **7** – Clarity **8** – Harmony	W
67.5°	☶ Gen **1** – Annoyance **3** – Sickness **4** – Disaster **9** – Adversity **2** – Vitality **6** – Health **7** – Harmony **8** – Clarity	☵ Kan **1** – Clarity **3** – Health **4** – Vitality **9** – Harmony **2** – Disaster **6** – Sickness **7** – Adversity **8** – Annoyance	☰ Qian **1** – Sickness **3** – Annoyance **4** – Adversity **9** – Disaster **2** – Harmony **6** – Clarity **7** – Vitality **8** – Health	292.5°
NE	22.5°	N	337.5°	NW

24 Mountains

Gua	Direction	24 Mountains				Degree
☵ Kan	North	N1	壬	ren	Yang Water	337.5 - 352.5
		N2	子	zi	Rat - Yang Water	352.5 - 7.5
		N3	癸	gui	Yin Water	7.5 - 22.5
☶ Gen	Northeast	NE1	丑	chou	Ox - Yin Earth$_{Water}$	22.5 - 37.5
		NE2	艮	gen	Gen - Earth	37.5 - 52.5
		NE3	寅	yin	Tiger - Yang Wood	52.5 - 67.5
☳ Zhen	East	E1	甲	jia	Yang Wood	67.5 - 82.5
		E2	卯	mao	Rabbit - Yin Wood	82.5 - 97.5
		E3	乙	yi	Yin Wood	97.5 - 112.5
☴ Xun	Southeast	SE1	辰	chen	Dragon - Yang Earth$_{Wood}$	112.5 - 127.5
		SE2	巽	xun	Xun - Wood	127.5 - 142.5
		SE3	巳	si	Snake - Yin Fire	142.5 - 157.5
☲ Li	South	S1	丙	bing	Yang Fire	157.5 - 172.5
		S2	午	wu	Horse - Yang Fire	172.5 - 187.5
		S3	丁	ding	Yin Fire	187.5 - 202.5
☷ Kun	Southwest	SW1	未	wei	Goat - Yin Earth$_{Fire}$	202.5 - 217.5
		SW2	坤	kun	Kun - Earth	217.5 - 232.5
		SW3	申	shen	Monkey - Yang Metal	232.5 - 247.5
☱ Dui	West	W1	庚	gen	Yang Metal	247.5 - 262.5
		W2	酉	you	Rooster - Yin Metal	262.5 - 277.5
		W3	辛	xin	Yin Metal	277.5 - 292.5
☰ Qian	Northwest	NW1	戌	xu	Dog - Yang Earth$_{Metal}$	292.5 - 307.5
		NW2	乾	qian	Qian - Metal	307.5 - 322.5
		NW3	亥	hai	Pig - Yin Water	322.5 - 337.5

Ba Gua – The Eight Trigrams

Trigram	☵ 坎 Kan	☳ 震 Zhen	☴ 巽 Xun	☲ 離 Li	☷ 坤 Kun	☰ 乾 Qian	☱ 兑 Dui	☶ 艮 Gen
Picture	Water	Thunder	Wind	Fire	Earth	Heaven	Lake	Mountain
Element	Water	Wood	Wood	Fire	Earth	Metal	Metal	Earth
Quality	Abysmal	Exciting	Gentle	Clinging	Receptive	Creative	Joyous	Quiescent
Person	Middle Son	Oldest Son	Oldest Daughter	Middle Daughter	Father	Mother	Youngest Daughter	Youngest Son
Luo Shu	1	3	4	9	2	6	7	8
Direction	North	East	Southeast	South	Southwest	Northwest	West	Northeast
Season	Winter	Spring	Early Summer	Summer	Late Summer	Late Autumn	Autumn	Early Spring
He Tu Number	6	4	5	3	8	1	2	7
He Tu Direction	West	Northeast	Southwest	East	North	South	Southeast	Northwest
Group	East Group				West Group			

Luo Shu

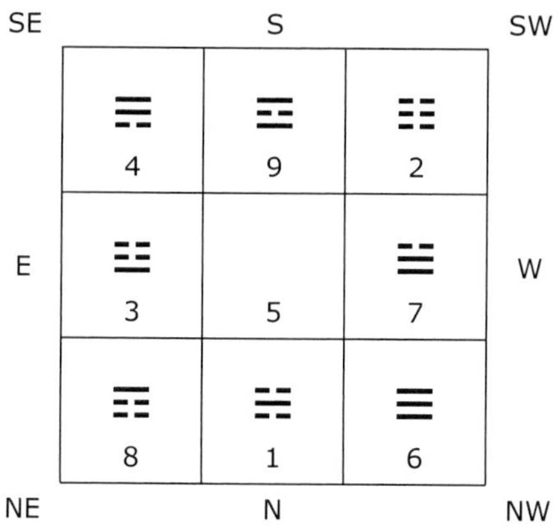

He Tu

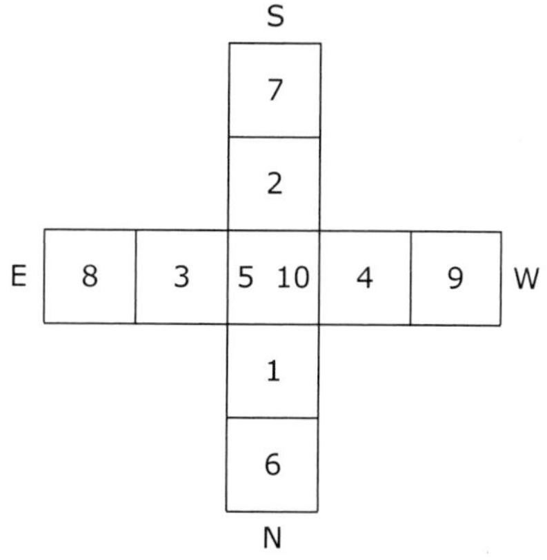

Cycles and Periods

Cycle	Period	Year	Gua		
Upper	1	1504 - 1523	☵	Kan	坎
	2	1524 - 1543	☷	Kun	坤
	3	1544 - 1563	☳	Zhen	震
Middle	4	1564 - 1583	☴	Xun	巽
	5	1584 - 1603	-		
	6	1604 - 1623	☰	Qian	乾
Lower	7	1624 - 1643	☱	Dui	兑
	8	1644 - 1663	☶	Gen	艮
	9	1664 - 1683	☲	Li	離
Upper	1	1684 - 1703	☵	Kan	坎
	2	1704 - 1723	☷	Kun	坤
	3	1724 - 1743	☳	Zhen	震
Middle	4	1744 - 1763	☴	Xun	巽
	5	1764 - 1783	-		
	6	1784 - 1803	☰	Qian	乾
Lower	7	1804 - 1823	☱	Dui	兑
	8	1824 - 1843	☶	Gen	艮
	9	1844 - 1863	☲	Li	離
Upper	1	1864 - 1883	☵	Kan	坎
	2	1884 - 1903	☷	Kun	坤
	3	1904 - 1923	☳	Zhen	震
Middle	4	1924 - 1943	☴	Xun	巽
	5	1944 - 1963	-		
	6	1964 - 1983	☰	Qian	乾
Lower	7	1984 - 2003	☱	Dui	兑
	8	2004 - 2023	☶	Gen	艮
	9	2024 - 2043	☲	Li	離

Flying Stars

Within Flying Star Feng Shui, Xuan Kong Fei Xing, stars represent different qualities of qi. One of the elements is assigned to each star.

Star	Quality	Topic	Assessment
1 Water	Wisdom	success, love, leave, luck	favorable
2 Earth	Health	sickness, fertility, effectiveness	unfavorable
3 Wood	Courage	competition, argument, lawsuit, robbery	neutral
4 Wood	Knowledge	success, creativity, literature, romance	favorable
5 Earth	Perfection	sickness, obstacles, catastrophes	unfavorable
6 Metal	Authority	power, dignity, stubbornness, destiny	favorable
7 Metal	Spirituality	art, speech, rivalry, fight	neutral
8 Earth	Wealth	prosperity, loneliness, children's disease	favorable
9 Fire	Power	promotion, litigation, madness, fire	favorable

Starting with the star in the center, the other stars "fly" into their directions. The magical square Luo Shu is the "basic flight plan".

SE	S	SW
4	9	2
3	**5**	7
8	1	6
NE	N	NW

Rows: E (left) – W (right)

Luo Shu

SE	S	SW
9	5	7
8	**1**	3
4	6	2
NE	N	NW

SE	S	SW
1	6	8
9	**2**	4
5	7	3
NE	N	NW

SE	S	SW
2	7	9
1	**3**	5
6	8	4
NE	N	NW

SE	S	SW
3	8	1
2	**4**	6
7	9	5
NE	N	NW

SE	S	SW
5	1	3
4	**6**	8
9	2	7
NE	N	NW

SE	S	SW
6	2	4
5	**7**	9
1	3	8
NE	N	NW

SE	S	SW
7	3	5
6	**8**	1
2	4	9
NE	N	NW

SE	S	SW
8	4	6
7	**9**	2
3	5	1
NE	N	NW

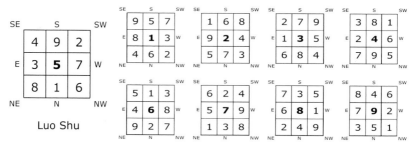

Year, month and day each have their own pertaining star, given at the right top for every day in the calendar. The star of the year has the biggest impact, the monthly star sets the main focus, and the daily star shows the actual outcome. For a detailed analysis the corresponding star squares are put onto each other. This way you get a specific statement for each compass direction.

Example 4 – 2 – 9

upper	daily star	*9*
middle	monthly star	2
lower	yearly star	**4**

	SE	S	SW	
	8 1 **3**	*4* 6 **8**	*6* 8 **1**	
E	*7* 9 **2**	*9* 2 **4**	*2* 4 **6**	W
	3 5 **7**	*5* 7 **9**	*1* 3 **5**	
	NE	N	NW	

Please note that south is on top of the magical square Luo Shu!

Flying Stars 2022

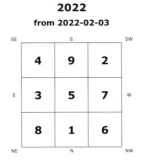

2021
from 2021-02-03

SE		S		SW
	5	**1**	**3**	
E	**4**	**6**	**8**	W
	9	**2**	**7**	
NE		N		NW

2022
from 2022-02-03

SE		S		SW
	4	**9**	**2**	
E	**3**	**5**	**7**	W
	8	**1**	**6**	
NE		N		NW

2023
from 2023-02-04

SE		S		SW
	3	**8**	**1**	
E	**2**	**4**	**6**	W
	7	**9**	**5**	
NE		N		NW

December 2021
from 2021-12-06

SE		S		SW
	3 **5**	8 **1**	1 **3**	
E	2 **4**	4 **6**	6 **8**	W
	7 **9**	9 **2**	5 **7**	
NE		N		NW

January 2022
from 2022-01-05

SE		S		SW
	2 **5**	7 **1**	9 **3**	
E	1 **4**	3 **6**	5 **8**	W
	6 **9**	8 **2**	4 **7**	
NE		N		NW

February 2022
from 2022-02-03

SE		S		SW
	1 **4**	6 **9**	8 **2**	
E	9 **3**	2 **5**	4 **7**	W
	5 **8**	7 **1**	3 **6**	
NE		N		NW

March 2022
from 2022-03-05

SE		S		SW
	9 **4**	5 **9**	7 **2**	
E	8 **3**	1 **5**	3 **7**	W
	4 **8**	6 **1**	2 **6**	
NE		N		NW

April 2022
from 2022-04-04

SE		S		SW
	8 **4**	4 **9**	6 **2**	
E	7 **3**	9 **5**	2 **7**	W
	3 **8**	5 **1**	1 **6**	
NE		N		NW

May 2022
from 2022-05-05

SE		S		SW
	7 **4**	3 **9**	5 **2**	
E	6 **3**	8 **5**	1 **7**	W
	2 **8**	4 **1**	9 **6**	
NE		N		NW

Monthly star upper left
Yearly star lower right

Flying Stars 2022

June 2022
from 2022-06-05

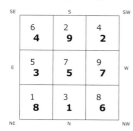

SE		S		SW
	6 **4**	2 **9**	4 **2**	
E	5 **3**	7 **5**	9 **7**	W
	1 **8**	3 **1**	8 **6**	
NE		N		NW

July 2022
from 2022-07-07

SE		S		SW
	5 **4**	1 **9**	3 **2**	
E	4 **3**	6 **5**	8 **7**	W
	9 **8**	2 **1**	7 **6**	
NE		N		NW

August 2022
from 2022-08-07

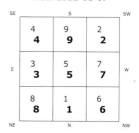

SE		S		SW
	4 **4**	9 **9**	2 **2**	
E	3 **3**	5 **5**	7 **7**	W
	8 **8**	1 **1**	6 **6**	
NE		N		NW

September 2022
from 2022-09-07

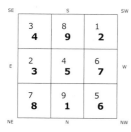

SE		S		SW
	3 **4**	8 **9**	1 **2**	
E	2 **3**	4 **5**	6 **7**	W
	7 **8**	9 **1**	5 **6**	
NE		N		NW

October 2022
from 2022-10-08

SE		S		SW
	2 **4**	7 **9**	9 **2**	
E	1 **3**	3 **5**	5 **7**	W
	6 **8**	8 **1**	4 **6**	
NE		N		NW

November 2022
from 2022-11-07

SE		S		SW
	1 **4**	6 **9**	8 **2**	
E	9 **3**	2 **5**	4 **7**	W
	5 **8**	7 **1**	3 **6**	
NE		N		NW

December 2022
from 2022-12-07

SE		S		SW
	9 **4**	5 **9**	7 **2**	
E	8 **3**	1 **5**	3 **7**	W
	4 **8**	6 **1**	2 **6**	
NE		N		NW

January 2023
from 2023-01-05

SE		S		SW
	8 **4**	4 **9**	6 **2**	
E	7 **3**	9 **5**	2 **7**	W
	3 **8**	5 **1**	1 **6**	
NE		N		NW

February 2023
from 2023-02-04

SE		S		SW
	7 **3**	3 **8**	5 **1**	
E	6 **2**	8 **4**	1 **6**	W
	2 **7**	4 **9**	9 **5**	
NE		N		NW

Monthly star upper left
Yearly star lower right

Feng Shui

Feng Shui

... wind and water

You waist a lot of time? Your life is at a standstill? Nothing seems to work right? Your nights are restless and you cannot concentrate? You feel listless?

The flow of qi in your surroundings is disturbed and has a negative influence on your energetic potential. At this point feng shui will come to your aid.

Feng shui produces harmoniously flowing qi specifically suited to a person.

By performing simple, but at times also fundamental changes to house and garden, the flow of qi, the energy and vitality of the universe, is activated and induced.

When searching for a property, planning a garden, a new home or furnishing an office, considering the principles of feng shui beforehand is the ideal way to start.

The Person

... is in the focus

Each human being requires qi, the energy and vitality of the universe, gained from nourishment, breath, light and warmth. But every person has individual, unique requirements.

The individual traits of a person, including strengths and weaknesses and each person's unique way of life are the starting point for any feng shui consultation. The individually advantageous compass directions for vitality, health, family life and clarity are identified. A correct positioning of a desk or a bed strengthens concentrated work and restful sleep. Supportive colors, shapes and behavior mode promote growth of a person.

Strengths and weaknesses of a character and life themes are considered to shape a personal advice concerning both surroundings and way of life.

Feng Shui

The House

... strengthens the person

Feng shui uses the qi received from the landscape and the home to nourish the human being.

Feng shui examines the position of the home and the quality of the entering qi as well as its distribution within the house. If the qi entering the house is of inferior quality, than only that qi will be dispensed throughout the house. Qi that flows too rapidly as well as stagnating qi should be avoided. Feng shui clears away obstacles and regulates the flow of qi.

Time influences the qi of the interior as well. As time goes by, room balance needs to be revisited to compensate.

A skillful set-up of the interior, including appropriate furniture and choice of color, structure and material, improves the flow of qi, increases the qi quality and brings harmony to home and family. Distinct decorations promote important aspects of daily life.

The Place of Work

... nourishes the person

Business feng shui is based on the same principles as feng shui for a home. The employees profit from the qi surrounding the business site as well as from the interior arrangements.

The entrance to an office, place of business or store is of the utmost importance. The higher the number of people entering through the doorway, the greater its influence on sales. In retail stores placement of the cash register is also significant.

Each employee requires a dedicated setup of his place of work, desk or counter to strengthen him. If work is done with higher motivation and pleasure, the business grows and prospers.

In contrast to home feng shui, where vitality, health and harmony between residents are of utmost importance to be considered, the principal aim for business feng shui consultation is to increase business and profits.

Feng Shui

The Garden

... guardian of the home

Wind and water shape our surroundings. Water, brooks and paths guide qi through the garden. Stones, hills and mountains stabilize the qi. Light and shadow, form, color and plant fragrance modify its quality.

Feng shui assesses the position of the home and its surroundings. Through the correct positioning of rocks and plants the house is shielded, through plants, water and pathways the qi is enhanced and led into the house. Feng shui utilizes the impact of water and rocks to establish the energy of the house's interiors.

A running brook in the vicinity of the front entrance, called water dragon, carries luck, health and wealth into the home.

Harmony evolves from the relationship between a person and his garden. That is why a feng shui garden is designed to individually suit person, site and time.

Feng Shui 2022

The Chinese year 壬寅 (ren yin) is the year of the water tiger and is influenced by the star Lian Zhen (5). It is characterized by extreme contrasts. Self-expression and exercise of power meet foresight and justice. On the one hand, the struggle for resources and wealth, influence and power is intensifying; on the other hand, there is increasing commitment to improving living conditions for everyone and protecting the planet and its inhabitants. This year everyone is asked to leave their comfort zone, take a closer look and form an own independent opinion. Then take your stand with courage and prudence and implement it creatively with heart and mind. Encounter difficulties with discipline and justice. Concentrate on creative solutions. Enjoy art and literature and rejoice in the beauty of the world.

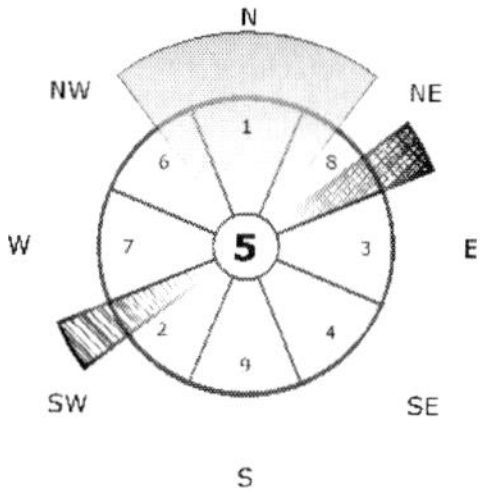

Each year you should pay attention to special compass directions. The grand duke **Tai Sui** in the northeast (52.5°–67.5°) is the strongest energy of the year. He does not like to be disturbed. Do not move earth or make renovations in his direction. The year breaker **Sui Po** in the southwest (232.5°–247.5°) is the weakest energy of the year. He is in conflict with the Tai Sui and is better not disturbed as well. The three devils **San Sha** in the north (322.5°–37.5°) are allies of the Tai Sui. Also avoid renovations and excavations in their presence. The **Five Yellow** in the center is the most difficult energy of the year. Keep the center clean, tidy and bright and ensure peace and harmony.

Direction	**Star**	**Energy**	**Measure**
North	1	wisdom, career	water, activity
Northeast	8	wealth	bowl with coins, activity
East	3	quarrel, robbery	plants, tranquility
Southeast	4	creativity, romance	plants, activity
South	9	success, promotion	light, activity
Southwest	2	sickness	avoid, tranquility
West	7	rivalry, spirituality	bowl with coins, tranquility
Northwest	6	authority, stubbornness	terracotta, stones, tranquility

The activating measures light and water are useful for the energy of the year, however they can conflict with the basic energy of the house.

Ba Zi – Chinese Astrology

Ba Zi

...the signs of destiny

The cosmic trinity tian - ren - di, heaven - man - earth, is the foundation of Chinese astrology. Heaven and earth manifest themselves in a human being at the moment of his birth. This individual energy is expressed by the four pillars or eight signs (ba zi) of destiny (suan ming).

The Chinese birth horoscope consists of four combinations of heavenly stems and earthly branches. The distribution of yin and yang, the five elements and the relations between them inform about the individual traits of a person with strengths, weaknesses and potentials. The supporting and restricting energies, attitudes and behavior of a person's life are derived from the structure of the horoscope.

The palaces of destiny describe a person's fundamental attitude towards life as well as the energetic impact of different aspects of life on him. Highlighting strengths and potentials as well as obstacles and dangers facilitates to focus on specific life themes to enhance love and family life, profession and self-realization.

The pillars of luck give the energetic weather forecast on your life path. During rainfall you can stand in the pouring rain, take an umbrella or enjoy your home. Wind from the front slows down, wind from the back spurs on. Your individual position makes the difference. The art of a good life consists of a clever and skillful use of the energies of heaven and earth.

The flowing years analyze your actual life situation and enable a detailed planning of your activities during the next days, months and years.

For Chinese people destiny is a mixture of determination and free will, a harmony of 30% heaven's qi, 30% earth's qi and 40% human qi. Heaven's qi is utilized by date selection, feng shui influences the earth qi, but a human being determines his destiny also significantly by his deeds.

The signs of destiny offer the chance of getting a clear picture of one's own strengths, weaknesses and potentials. You can then use your free will to choose your way and promote your growth. From the Chinese point of view, wisdom consists of the ability to look at oneself with a smile and to make the best of one's fate.

* Calculate your ba zi on www.wangnick.com/software_4pillarscalculator.htm.

Ba Zi

The Chinese birth horoscope consists of four pillars for hour, day, month and year respectively. Each pillar contains a heavenly stem and an earthly branch. These are a synthesis of yin or yang and one of the five elements.

	Hour	Day	Month	Year
Heavenly Stem				
Earthly Branch				

Calculate your own Ba Zi and enter the characters here.* The Chinese zodiac sign is the earthy branch of the year. The most important sign of a Ba Zi is the heavenly stem of the day, the gray-shaded day master. It represents the individual. All other signs are interpreted by reference to him, and each of the five elements is associated with a factor.

The aim in life is a well-balanced relationship between yin and yang and the five elements. What about the balance between activity and tranquility? Where is excess, where deficit? Avoid clashes, and make dedicated use of those days that either contain or produce your missing elements or control your overwhelming elements, to balance your Ba Zi.

Elements – Factors

Factor \ Day master	**Wood**	**Fire**	**Earth**	**Metal**	**Water**
Identity	Wood	Fire	Earth	Metal	Water
Performance	Fire	Earth	Metal	Water	Wood
Wealth	Earth	Metal	Water	Wood	Fire
Influence	Metal	Water	Wood	Fire	Earth
Resource	Water	Wood	Fire	Earth	Metal

Clash

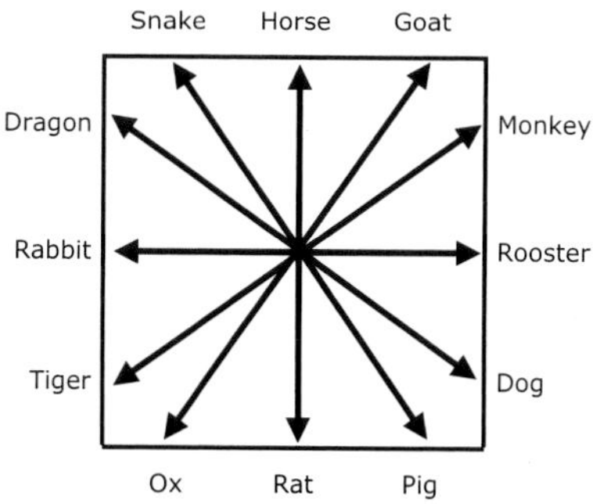

Rat	↔	Horse
Ox	↔	Goat
Tiger	↔	Monkey
Rabbit	↔	Rooster
Dragon	↔	Dog
Snake	↔	Pig

Ba Zi 2022

Rat

Auspicious Relationships:	Rat, Monkey, Dragon, Ox
Unfavorable Relationships:	Horse, Rooster, Rabbit

This year, the curious and passionate Rat has the opportunity to put long-held ambitions and creative ideas into practice. With self-confidence and standing it commits itself to its dreams and works consistently and purposefully towards its goals. Mindfulness and empathy are particularly important in personal relationships so that the required autonomy is not experienced by others as a rejection. This year brings movement into the life of the Rat, be it through travel, steps on the path to self-realization, new ideas, or unexpected joys of love.

Ox

Auspicious Relationships:	Rooster, Snake, Ox, Rat
Unfavorable Relationships:	Goat, Dragon, Dog

This year, the traditional and dutiful ox has good opportunities to advance professionally. In doing so, it does not shy away from confrontation and often approaches its co-workers in an undiplomatic or even hostile manner. Its persistent focus on work eventually brings the ox the desired personal and financial recognition. In his private life his directness and stubbornness threaten to marginalize him, so the ox is well advised to take care of his family lovingly and sensitively.

Tiger

Auspicious Relationships:	Horse, Tiger, Dog
Unfavorable Relationships:	Monkey, Pig, Snake

The courageous and passionate tiger goes to work inventive and determined this year. It is important that it thinks carefully about what it wants to achieve and that it has its goals clearly in mind. If the Tiger plans its course of action thoroughly and implements it in a focused and consistent manner, it can achieve a lot. The goal-oriented and aggressive action necessary to achieve its ambitions can lead to problems with colleagues and friends. Here the tiger is challenged to develop his diplomatic skills, otherwise it will make many enemies. This is especially important in private life. If the tiger combines its self-confidence with empathy and intuition, it can strengthen and enjoy its personal contacts.

Rabbit

Auspicious Relationships: Rabbit, Pig, Goat, Dog

Unfavorable Relationships: Rooster, Horse, Rat

The reserved and distant rabbit is challenged this year to reconcile with offended friends and business partners. If conflicts are not avoided but mindfully endured, it will learn a lot about itself. Support comes from unexpected sources. This year, the Rabbit's attractiveness is increased significantly and its personal relationships will develop.

Dragon

Auspicious Relationships: Rat, Monkey, Dragon, Rooster

Unfavorable Relationships: Dog, Ox

The creative and optimistic dragon is bursting with new ideas. This year there is a chance that a project, thought impossible, has an unexpected chance of success. If the dragon clearly defines its objectives, a solution will be found, but it is important to work consistently to achieve them. Learning comes easily to the Dragon this year. It can satisfy his thirst for adventure by traveling.

Snake

Auspicious Relationships: Rooster, Snake, Ox

Unfavorable Relationships: Pig, Monkey, Tiger

For the sensitive and graceful snake it is a year full of obstacles and delays. Cooperation with colleagues turns out to be difficult. Misunderstandings, injuries and open conflict arise. There are also problems in its partnership that should not be ignored. The snake can counter all these difficulties with patience, understanding and absolute honesty. If the snake is clear about its red lines, remains true to itself and acts justly, it will receive support, succeed again, and will lead a happy life.

Horse

Auspicious Relationships:	Horse, Tiger, Dog, Goat
Unfavorable Relationships:	Rat, Rabbit

This year the sociable and adventurous horse can undock and set out for new shores. It is full of enthusiasm and expands its contacts, both professional and private. By traveling, especially to unknown places, the horse broadens its horizons and opens up to new possibilities. It receives strength and support, and its efforts are amply rewarded. The female horse has a chance to find a partner, but it must be willing to take the first step.

Goat

Auspicious Relationships:	Rabbit, Pig, Goat, Horse
Unfavorable Relationships:	Ox, Dog

The amiable and active goat expects a year of successful change. The headwind that was felt last year is subsiding, outdated customs are overcome, plans for the future succeed, and the commendable achievements gained though its steady work are appropriately rewarded in good time.

Monkey

Auspicious Relationships:	Rat, Monkey, Dragon
Unfavorable Relationships:	Tiger, Snake

The monkey, which despite its playful nature plans ahead intelligently, will face challenges this year. Superiors have unrealistic expectations regarding the monkeys design, creation and implementation of new ideas and products, leading to conflict. If the monkey succeeds in enjoying the constant flow of new suggestions and also in staying flexible to possibly find alternatives elsewhere, success and prosperity will beckon in the end.

Rooster

Auspicious Relationships: Rooster, Snake, Ox, Dragon

Unfavorable Relationships: Rabbit, Rat

This year, the perceptive and self-confident rooster has particularly great stamina and assertiveness. With power, efficiency and strategic thinking, it can advance his career. Extreme caution is required though in all financial dealings. The Rooster receives help and support over the course of the year and can strengthen and enjoy its relationships.

Dog

Auspicious Relationships: Horse, Tiger, Dog, Rabbit

Unfavorable Relationships: Dragon, Goat, Ox

Many opportunities are opening up for the determined and loyal dog this year, and it knows how to take advantage of them. Its efforts over the past few years are now bearing fruit. It can develop professionally, also because it learns easily and efficiently. It has a lot of power and can take care of the essential things in its life and make trend-setting decisions. People will flock towards it. With its good intuition, the dog will make new friends, a male dog has the chance to find its partner.

Pig

Auspicious Relationships: Rabbit, Pig, Goat

Unfavorable Relationships: Snake, Tiger

For the wise and vigilant pig it is a year of retreat and gathering strength. All professional change will involve great difficulties and will not bring the desired success. It therefore makes more sense to focus on developing and promoting long-term strategies. The pig should be especially careful in all financial matters and postpone important decisions. The focus this year is on learning, self-development and creative expression. In its private life the pig can enjoy its new self-confidence and the pleasures in life.

Notes

Notes

Notes

Notes

Notes

Notes

Notes

Notes

Notes

Notes

Notes

Notes

Addresses

A

B

Addresses

C

D

Addresses

E

F

Addresses

G

H

Addresses

I

J

Addresses

K

L

Addresses

M

N

Addresses

O

P

Q

Addresses

R

S

Addresses

T

U

Addresses

V

W

Addresses

X

Y

Z

Dispersed by wind … Qi … gathered by water

Life develops from the harmonic flow of Qi!

Anne Rosa Wangnick Consulting

MSc in Computer Science, Reiki Master, Shaman

searches for backgrounds and connections
has experience in modernisation of old cottages and garden design
lives with husband and cats in the Eifel/Germany

Individually calculated and designed calendars

Date selection
- for business opening, contract signature, project kick-off
- for marriage, christening, house building, house purchase
- appropriate for several persons

Selection of proper locations for important events

Feng Shui for business, office, store

Feng Shui for house and garden

Garden design
- specialised in water design (water dragon)

Chinese astrology
- personal development and choice of career
- horoscopes for partnership

I Ching oracle

Software for 10.000 year calendar, Chinese astrology, date selection

Presentations, seminars, workshops

Anne Rosa Wangnick Consulting
Lammersdorfer Str. 61
D-52159 Roetgen-Rott
tel: +49 (0)2471 134989
mail: anne@wangnick.com
www.wangnick.com

Books – Products

Books ... compact knowledge

Custom built with your own content by Anne Rosa Wangnick
Hot off the press by amazon

Moments of Luck
Feng Shui and Ba Zi Calendar

Feng Shui Reference
With Chinese Lunar Calendar 1900 – 2099

Wannianli – Ten Thousand Year Calendar
Chinese Solar and Lunar Calendar 1900 – 2099
With Feng Shui and Ba Zi Reference
Astronomically exact
In English with Chinese characters and Pinyin
Sorted according to the Western calendar year
Heavenly stem - earthly branch combination & lunar date per day
Moon phases, solar phases, flying stars, lunar mansions

Wannianli –1600 – 1899
Chinese Ten Thousand Year Calendar

Products ... custom made

Personal Feng Shui
With chinesischer Numerology

Internet-Calendars
Moments of Luck for days
Moments of Luck for hours
Solar and Lunar Calendar
Officers, Lunar Mansions, ...

時 運– Moments of Luck

Your Personal Calendar

... custom made

- Individually calculated for your birth date
- Moments of luck as intuitive symbols
  ♥ ♥̸ Love, € €̸ Money, ⏻ ⏻̸ Start, ✈ ✈̸ Travel, ϟ Conflict, ...
- Easy color coding for personal and general information
- Begin of the Chinese double hours as time on a sundial exactly calculated for your residence
- One week on two pages or one day per page in three sizes
- Duration 12, 15 or 18 months
- Free choice of period (for example birthday, wedding day)
- Explanation of the systems and feng shui tables in the appendix
- Personal dates and information can be imprinted
- Custom-made diary with artistic cover design
- Partnership diary for two persons
- Two ribbon page markers, book mark and insert pocket

Software

Free Software

... anytime and anywhere

Pillars of Destiny
Moments of Luck
Tong Shu with Officer and Lunar Mansion
Flying Stars of the Houes
Flying Stars of Time
Gua Number
Feng Shui Dimensions
Chinese Numerology
Life Path
Solar Time Calculator

Professional Software

... individual settings

Ba Zi professional

- Detailed Calculations
- Personal Term Definitions
- Different calendars and methods of calculation
- Astronomically precisely calculated solar time

www.wangnick.com/software_startseite.htm

Calendar Structure

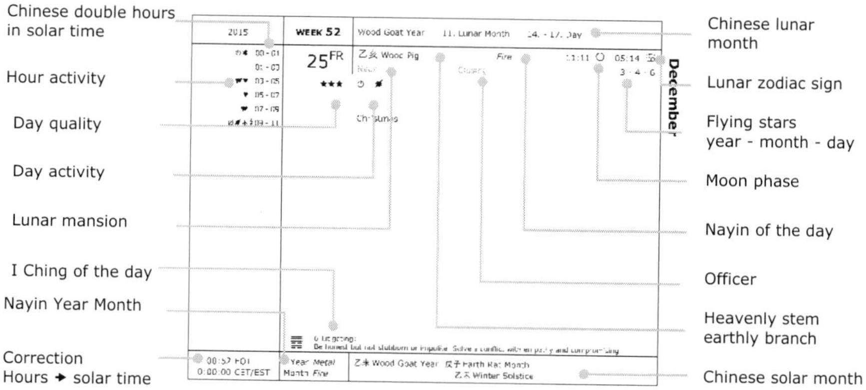

Auspicious	Activities	Avoid
✹	support	~~✹~~
❤❤	love, partnership, marriage	~~❤❤~~
♥	communication, negotiations, friends	~~♥~~
✈	travel	~~✈~~
⏻	start projects, business opening	~~⏻~~
€	money related affairs	~~€~~

Day Quality

ϟ	explosive energy
~~☆☆~~	very difficult day
~~☆~~	difficult day
★	average day
★★	good day
★★★	excellent day

Solar Time

Longitude correction .... min

www.wangnick.com/software_timecalculator.htm

Moon Phases

●	New Moon
☽	Waxing Moon
○	Full Moon
☾	Waning Moon

Zodiac Signs

♑	Capricorn	♋	Cancer
♒	Aquarius	♌	Leo
♓	Pisces	♍	Virgo
♈	Aries	♎	Libra
♉	Taurus	♏	Scorpio
♊	Gemini	♐	Sagittarius

Made in United States
North Haven, CT
04 February 2022

15626293R00115